L. E Jarvis Capt.
Cdn Trang Sch
Cdn. Army, Engla

ZERO HOURS

BOOKS BY
GUN BUSTER

Return via Dunkirk
Battle Dress
Zero Hours

Hodder and Stoughton

ZERO HOURS

BY
GUN BUSTER

London: HODDER & STOUGHTON, LIMITED

First printed November, 1942

———————————————

THE TYPOGRAPHY AND BINDING OF
THIS BOOK CONFORM TO THE
AUTHORISED ECONOMY STANDARD

*Made and Printed in Great Britain for Hodder & Stoughton, Limited, London
by Wyman & Sons Limited, London, Reading and Fakenham*

CONTENTS

THE Troop Commander, a happy youth with a good digestion and nothing on his conscience (so far as he was aware), passed easily from a dreamless sleep to wide wakefulness. He took a glance at his wrist-watch. It registered forty-five minutes to zero hour.

" Damn his adenoids," he exclaimed forcibly to himself. " They've done me out of a good half-hour."

Within the dark interior of the heavy infantry tank, in front of him just under his feet, the slumbering gunner, mouth wide open, continued to generate a particularly malevolent brand of snore. It seemed to arrive from far away in the depth of the throat with the scream of a 4.5 howitzer shell, and suddenly explode at the back of the nose with the nasty crack of one of those big German mortar bombs. At least, that was how it appeared to the warped mind of the Troop Commander.

He took another glance at his watch, considering whether he should try to make up the lost half-hour.

" Better not," he concluded. " I might oversleep myself."

It crossed his mind to jerk his knee into the gunner's back and tell him to cease fire and give the loader next to him a chance. But he discovered that the loader required no favours. He couldn't have slept more soundly if the gunner's barrage had been his own mother's lullaby.

" Marvellous . . ." commented the Troop Commander. " Well, if I can't get any more sleep I'll have some fresh air."

He readjusted the balaclava helmet beneath his beret, drew the sheepskin waistcoat tighter round him, opened the turret, and with head and shoulders projecting, surveyed the night. After a few seconds the inrush

7

of the bitterly cold air cut the gunner short in the middle of his mightiest effort.   He stirred restlessly, half unconscious of his surroundings.

" For Christ's sake shut that window, somebody," he pleaded dreamily.   " It's perishing."

" Oh, it's you, sir," he added resignedly, when he had unsealed his eyes.

The loader slept on, impervious to all distractions.

Except that the moon hung lower in the sky, the night was pretty much as they had left it a couple of hours before, when they had bedded down inside the tank to snatch a short spell of sleep before the assault on Bardia began.   Earlier, the squadron had crawled over the desert in the darkness from the south-east, and were now drawn up in battle-line on the open plain about two miles distant from the formidable tank ditch surrounding the Bardia defences.   " Thunderbolt," which was the Troop Commander's tank, occupied a position on the left of the line, and gazing out of the turret, he could distinguish the dark, shadowy shapes of the rest of the squadron rising from the grey moonlit desert on either side of him, like some strange fleet riding at anchor on a becalmed ocean.

" Peaceful enough now, sir," observed the gunner, leaning forward comfortably on his elbows.

Away to the left of them and straight ahead the night was lit up incessantly with terrific flashes.   Muffled booms echoed from the distance, and nearer at hand there followed violent explosions.   The ground reverberated beneath them.   It was the Navy shelling Bardia. Verey lights soared into the sky at frequent intervals and burst into a brilliance that temporarily outshone the moon.   They were followed by sharp bursts of machine-gun fire, punctuated by tracer bullets that seemed to streak the darkness with a fiery message, like live Morse.   Strings of flaming onions floated down from the black heavens over the town, and the heavy detonations of the R.A.F.'s bombs added the thunder of their echoes to that of the bursting shells.

8

"Peaceful enough. . . ."

But the Troop Commander never for a moment suspected the gunner of irony, even unconscious. As a matter of fact, he had more or less been thinking the same himself. Looking at the moon had reminded him, as moonlight nights always did, of his favourite " In such a night . . ." sequence from the " Merchant of Venice," and the haunting lines were still pervading his memory. He fully understood that the gunner was merely comparing the present with the immediate future. Judged by the hell that was about to envelop them, this certainly could be regarded as peace, despite the firework display in front.

"Yes," he agreed with a laugh. " But we'll have blood on the tracks by to-night."

"You bet we will," nodded the gunner.

"Blood on the tracks" was the battle-cry of the squadron—a grim figure of speech denoting desperate fighting. The Troop Commander hadn't any doubt but that it was highly appropriate in the present circumstances. To them had been allotted the task of cracking the tough nut of Bardia. Their orders were simple and precise. As soon as daylight broke, at zero hour, all the British 25-pounders and howitzer batteries in the rear were to concentrate in putting down a colossal barrage on a few hundred yards of front the other side of the twenty-foot wide enemy tank ditch. Simultaneously, the squadron was to tear, hell for leather, across the desert, straight in the direction of the narrow barrage, and crash through this isolated gap in the outer defences. Sappers had been busy the entire night making a rough causeway across the ditch at this spot. There would be no other way of crossing, save for this small strip. Once over the causeway they were to silence the nests of pill-boxes on the other side, and, leaving the infantry to do the mopping up, steer north-east with the purpose of cutting the Bardia defences in two. But they had to get over first.

"Blood on the tracks . . ."

9

Turning the matter over in his mind, the Troop Commander came to the conclusion that they could run into some big trouble at the tank ditch if anything happened to go wrong with the surprise. Every effort had been made to keep the enemy in ignorance that the big attack was to be delivered in this area. Long before the guns took up their final positions, loads of ammunition had been carted secretly across the desert night after night, and deposited by themselves in carefully concealed dumps. So that complete wireless silence should be maintained right up till zero hour, the tank crew commanders had received their orders in minutest detail before setting out for Bardia. All they awaited now was the final signal from the Squadron Commander.

The Troop Commander, always sceptical about well-kept secrets in war, hoped that this time his apprehensions would prove unjustified. Otherwise, he forecast a pretty mess, trying to force the narrow passage of the tank ditch in face of God-knows-what concentration of artillery and anti-tank gun-fire.

By now the night was over, and the desert began to reveal its monotonous miles in the pale daylight. From the turrets of all the other tanks protruded the heads and shoulders of the crew commanders, who had popped up for a final breather. The Troop Commander consulted his watch. Ten minutes to zero hour. . . .

" Just time for a last drink," he said to the gunner. " Get the thermos."

They swallowed down a few mouthfuls of warm tea, enlivened by a tot of whisky from the Troop Commander's flask.

" I'm feeling the cold, too," mentioned a voice from in front.

It was the driver who had emerged from his hatch under the two-pounder, and was standing up with his elbow resting on the gun.

The Troop Commander passed him down a drink. Within the tank the loader slumbered on.

Tied round the muzzle of the two-pounder was an

oily rag to keep out the sand. The driver commenced to take it off.

"Leave it," said the Troop Commander. "We'll be blowing it off in a minute."

Two minutes to zero. . . . They dived down within the tank again, and donned their earphones. The loader, as though he had timed himself to a nicety, woke up instantly alert and active and pushed a shell into the breech of the two-pounder. The Troop Commander switched on the wireless set and put it over to receive.

"Start up," he ordered the driver through the inter-com. And the engine roared its response.

Zero hour. . . .

"Tanks advance . . ." instantly came the awaited signal from the Squadron Commander, and the Troop Commander transmitted it :

"Two-Troop advance. . . . Good luck, boys. . . ."

And simultaneously the tremendous barrage started up, filling the sky with a mighty, prolonged thunder.

The Troop Commander had kept his flaps open and, begoggled, was still looking out of the turret as they moved off. Occasionally he waved his hand to the other crew commanders of the Troop as they swept forward line abreast over the desert with gathering speed. The din was deafening. Behind, the long, unbroken roar of the guns. Above, the scream of the shells. In front, the terrific explosions as the barrage warmed up in intensity. And, in addition, the noise of the tank engines themselves and the squeaking of the tracks.

A mile or so ahead the Troop Commander could see a small patch of ground that seemed to be alive with the flashes of the bursting shells. Darting, fiery tongues, pale yellow and reddish orange in hue, flickered like coloured lightning through the rising plumes of dust. That strip of land, sown with fire by the concentrated barrage, he knew to be his goal. He gazed on it, thrilled, fascinated, and slightly awe-struck.

The tanks were pounding along at twelve miles and the dust began to swirl up around the tracks as they tore on in the direction of the barrage. Soon little more could be seen of them than the turrets, and the muzzles of the two-pounders jutting out from the dust clouds. The Troop Commander now became conscious of something else besides the barrage. He was near enough to the outer defences to see the Italian guns firing at them from all along the front. A shell burst only fifty yards in front of him, followed by another, a little nearer but away to the right. He swung his periscope from side to side continually to see how the others were doing. So far everything appeared to have gone well. A queer kind of exultation seized him.

All around the shells were now bursting much closer, the splinters rattling against the armour of the tank. A smell of hot oil pervaded the interior as the engines warmed up. The gunner sat motionless with his eyes fastened to the gun periscope. The loader had switched on the festoon lighting, and it shed a faint gleam on the polished steel of the breech of the gun, and the brass of the shell cases ranged in their holes half-way up the turret. There was an atmosphere of calm and security within the tank that contrasted strangely with the whirlwind of death and destruction that raged outside.

Ahead of them the belt of flame and smoke grew larger and more awful in appearance as they raced towards it. It was only five hundred yards distant now. The Troop Commander could distinguish amidst the fountains of dust and sand hurled into the air by the exploding shells the darker shapes of huge lumps of stone and rock. He began to wonder anxiously what sort of a job the sappers had made of the tank ditch. Well, he would soon know now. . . .

A sickening crash sounded right on top of them, leaving them for a moment or two half stunned. The interior of the turret began to fill with a black acrid smoke. It had been hit by an H.E. shell. But no damage was done. The tank did not as much as waver in its course.

" Good old Thunderbolt ! . . ." cried the Troop Commander affectionately. " Thank God it didn't hit the track instead."

On they thundered into a deluge of fire from heavy machine-guns, the bullets pelting their armour like a fierce hail. Suddenly the patter was interrupted by a dull, ominous thud that reverberated through the tank, and shortly afterwards came another.

" Anti-tank shell, damn 'em ! . . ." muttered the Troop Commander. " Zig-zag a bit," he shouted to the driver, and the tank began to swerve from side to side. Glancing through the periscope, the Troop Commander saw that the rest of the troop were doing likewise.

By now they were on the lip of the ditch. The Troop Commander uttered a grunt of satisfaction. The sappers had done their job well. They had constructed a very passable roadway across, all ready for the tanks to walk in. Without a pause, Thunderbolt lurched over the edge of the ditch, bucketed as it dropped a few feet, then with an extra roar from the engine mounted the other slope. Right in front of them, under the blasting fury of the barrage, the ground heaved like a volcano in eruption, spouting up flame and smoke. They seemed about to plunge straight into the inferno.

" I hope they don't forget to lift at the right time," murmured the Troop Commander, a little dubiously.

And even as he was thinking it the barrage magically lifted and moved forward another hundred yards.

As the smoke drifted away he could see more clearly his immediate objective—the enemy fort about a furlong in front and slightly to his left. The fort comprised half a dozen concrete gun-posts " staggered " in such a way as to cover each other with their fire. They were all connected by underground tunnels which enabled the defenders to pass from one to the other when necessary, and were strongly fortified with light field guns, anti-tank guns and Bredas. The complete fort was surrounded by barbed wire, in front of which had been dug an anti-tank ditch, the top of which was covered with thin wooden slats, these in turn being covered with a layer of desert soil to make it appear solid earth. The slats would support the weight of men, but a tank would simply crash through into the ditch. All the intervening ground between the fort and the main ditch had been heavily sown with mines.

There were scores of these miniature fortresses dotted along the battle front. Having once broken through the gap, it was the business of the tanks to silence them without waste of time. Each tank selected the one nearest to it for its special attentions. "Thunderbolt," at a reduced speed, was warily threading its way through the minefield. Keeping an eye open for suspicious signs on the ground, the Troop Commander had constantly to change direction.

"Driver . . . left . . . left . . . steady," . . . he ordered, and the tank swerved to avoid a patch of sand that looked unnaturally smooth. Almost at once his periscope picked up a stretch of ground covered with white pebbles that seemed to him to be lying too lightly on the surface to be good.

"Driver . . . right . . . steady . . ." he shouted. And so it went on.

They proceeded forward through a storm of machine-gun bullets from the gun-posts in front. These worried them not at all. So far they had withheld their own fire. Suddenly the Troop Commander saw a red flash leap from the dark slit in the wall of one of them, and instantaneously an anti-tank shell hurled up the earth just in front of them.

"Two-pounder . . . traverse left . . . left . . ." he shouted to the gunner down the microphone, followed quickly by :

"Driver . . . right . . . steady . . ."

The gunner, with his forehead pressed against the shock-absorbing pad, peered along the sights.

"Two-pounder . . . left . . ." ordered the Troop Commander.

The slit in the gun-post moved on till it coincided with the intersection of the hair-lines in the gunner's periscope.

"You're on . . ." yelled the Troop Commander. "Driver . . . steady . . . Fire ! . . ."

Within the confined space of the tank the sharp crack of the gun echoed through their earphones. The loader slid another shell into the breech and tapped the gunner on the elbow to inform him of the fact.

"That's a good one!" exclaimed the Troop Commander, watching the result of the shot. The two-pounder shell had burst right on the slit. Chunks of concrete flew about in all directions.

"Two-pounder . . . left . . . left . . ." he chanted again as they continued to move slowly forward.

"Driver . . . steady . . ."

The gunner's right shoulder pressed against the leather crutch on the gun mounting, depressing it slightly. Once again the slit coincided with the cross-lines on the periscope.

"On. . . . Fire! . . ." shouted the Troop Commander.

This time a considerable hole appeared where the slit had been. The Troop Commander ordered a couple of bursts from the Besa, and after that there was no further reply from that quarter, though machine-gun fire still proceeded from the other posts. The Troop Commander now turned his attention to these, and the two-pounder cracked away as fast as it was loaded. The empty shell-cases shot back automatically against the steel shield in front of the commander's stomach and dropped with a rattle into the canvas bag beneath. The unmistakable odour of cordite mingled with the smell of hot oil inside the tank. The atmosphere had become so warm that the occupants were sweating under the extra clothing they had put on against the night cold. Not that they noticed it in the excitement.

At last the tank came to a standstill at the edge of the tank trap that encircled the group of gun-posts. The fire from these had by now completely died down. The Troop Commander, inspecting his work with satisfaction through the periscope, suddenly saw detachments of Australian infantry appear as if from nowhere on both sides of the tank. Rifles at the ready, they darted forward without hesitation over the slat-covered tank trap, cut their way through the barbed wire, and surrounded each post. Through the slits in the walls they tossed hand-grenades. A series of muffled explosions followed. Then there was silence. After a few moments a dozen or so of the infantrymen dived down the entrance to the underground tunnel to winkle out such of the occupants as still survived. Two or three minutes passed before they reappeared at the other end of the tunnel, shepherding in front of their bayonet points a miserable group of dirty unshaven prisoners clad in ragged dark, olive-green uniforms. Most of them were hatless. They had tied white handkerchiefs to their wrists, and were holding up their hands in token of surrender. A sort of blank, dazed terror fixed every face rigid, as though with a mask. They numbered thirty, all told, and some of the younger ones were sobbing in a queer gasping, mechanical way that seemed hardly human.

The Troop Commander was not inclined to waste sympathy upon enemies in the heat of battle. But it did occur to him that he had never before seen such a broken collection of human beings still calling themselves live men.

"That barrage has smashed them completely. There isn't a nerve left among the lot of 'em. . . . And I expect we've helped a bit," he thought, not without a certain mild satisfaction.

It was time for him to repeat the performance. Three hundred yards farther on, to the right, lay another nest of gun-posts, and he took this for his next quarry.

"Driver . . . advance . . . six . . ." he shouted down the microphone, keeping the speed down to six miles per hour so that he could safely negotiate the minefield. "Right . . . right . . . steady."

As the tank moved on little groups of the infantry accompanied it, grinning all over their faces with delight and making the "thumbs-up" signal to the unseen occupants. Some of the Australians, in their exhilaration, began to run towards the fort without waiting for the support of the tank.

" Damn fools . . . Can't they wait a second . . . ? " exclaimed the Troop Commander, irritably. " They're asking for it . . ."

In a moment or two they got it. The machine-guns in front suddenly opened fire, and the Troop Commander saw through his periscope four of the venturesome infantrymen stagger and drop.

" Two-pounder . . . right . . . right . . ." he shouted.

" Driver . . . steady . . .

" You're on . . . Fire . . .! "

Inside the tank the crack of their own shell was almost obliterated by a resounding thud as an anti-tank shell hit them on the armour plating just above the driver. Another followed almost immediately, ricochetting off its side. The Troop Commander had detected the flashes from two different gun posts.

" Couple of Ants . . ." he shouted to the gunner. " We've got to stop 'em quickly . . . Take 'em one at a time . . .

" Driver . . . zig-zag . . .

" Two-pounder . . . traverse left . . . On . . .

" Driver . . . steady . . .

" Fire . . .! "

The shell burst on top of the gun post, and two more landed on the same spot. When the smoke and dust had cleared away the Troop Commander came to the conclusion he hadn't any more to worry about in that direction. He turned his attention to the other danger point.

" Two-pounder . . . traverse right . . . right . . ."

By now the tank had covered nearly a hundred yards of the distance from the fort. For the time being, the Troop Commander's preoccupation with the anti-tank guns had been such as to distract his mind from the dangerous nature of the ground they were passing over. Suddenly he bethought himself to give it half-an-eye. As he did so two tufts of camel thorn that stood right in their path only a few yards away, with the sand heaped up innocently round the roots as though blown there by the wind, gently laid themselves flat. Some violent vibration of the ground had shaken them from their artificial position.

The Troop Commander needed nothing more to tell him that they were practically on top of a mine. No time remained for thought.

" Driver . . . Mine . . . Left . . . left . . . left . . . " he yelled frantically down the microphone, in a rush of words.

Alive to the emergency the driver planted his two feet firmly on the floor, jerked his head back, and stiffened his body to brace himself for the sudden swerve. With both hands he tugged on the left steering tiller, " breaking its neck." The tank executed a mighty lurch at an angle of over forty-five degrees from its former direction.

At the same instant the Troop Commander uttered a cry of horror. Up from the bottom of the pane of his periscope, like monstrosities in an aquarium, swam four heads and shoulders, and four pairs of raised hands, with white rags tied round the wrists. They were visible in the periscope only for a second. Then they sank down out of sight leaving the pane clear again. But the dreadful vision had persisted long enough for the Troop Commander to have stamped on his mind something he would never forget . . . Eyes bursting from their sockets with worse than terror. Lips parted to shriek, but unable to. Ghastly green faces . . .

They disappeared. The tank rolled on.

" My God . . . ! " groaned the Troop Commander, horror-stricken. " And they wanted to surrender . . ."

He struggled to blot out the dreadful picture that rose in his imagination. He could feel his temples beating . . . Beating in an insistent rhythm . . .

" Blood on the tracks . . . Blood on the tracks . . ."

Never again a mere figure of speech . . .

All had been a matter of a second or two. When the Troop Commander collected himself, he found that the tank had come to a stop. Thinking that, like himself, the driver had been temporarily overcome by the horror he began to shout to him furiously down the microphone :

" Advance . . . advance . . . Obey my orders . . . Advance . . ."

The driver was merely waiting for a red film that obscured his periscope to drain down to the bottom and give him a clear view.

" Advance . . ." the Troop Commander continued to yell. " It can't be helped . . . It was nobody's fault . . ."

As he uttered the words he felt as though he were addressing something inside himself, on his own behalf.

The tank moved on again.

" Two-pounder . . . traverse right . . . right . . ." the Troop Commander commenced shouting to the gunner.

His voice sounded normal again. But the words he was hearing were not those of the command.

They hammered deep down within his ears :

" *Blood on the tracks . . . Blood on the tracks . . .*"

II—COMPANY FOR ONE

FOR the moment the machine-gun platoon lying out in the desert in front of Bardia was enjoying a quiet spell. That is, if you left out of consideration the coveys of heavy shells from a distant Italian battery that continually screamed over their heads. But the machine-gun platoon wasn't worrying about these. Occasionally a shell did burst a few hundred yards to their rear. hurling up a cloud of smoke and sand. But the majority went right on. The machine-gunners knew that it wasn't their packet this time. Probably the artillery behind were getting it.

For several days detachments of infantry had been gradually pushing forward towards the outer defences of Bardia, driving in the enemy outposts and slowly moving into positions to make the final grand assault upon the town. As the infantry crept up the machine-

gunners followed close behind ready to give them covering fire whenever they ran up against difficult opposition.
By now the machine-gun platoon had reached its final
position. They had dug-in and sandbagged, put down
fixed lines for the four guns, and settled down to wait
till the big attack was put in. And what pleased them
much was that they seemed to have escaped observation by the enemy.

"A machine-gun found is a machine-gun lost," was
their favourite paradox.

Well, so far they hadn't been found . . . The shells
passing over head on some other errand told them that.

It was the middle of the afternoon, sunny, but cold
enough to make the gunners feel the benefit of their
cardigans as they lay tucked in the gun positions, chatting and smoking, with a light breeze every now and
then distributing the desert dust all over them. The
two sections of the platoon were about a hundred yards
apart, and so flat to the ground that they were hardly
visible to one another. A distance of some twenty yards
separated each gun of the sections. A good way back
their vehicles were concealed behind some low sand
dunes, ready for the move forward when the zero hour
came. In front of them, for nearly a mile, they gazed
out over flat, dun desert, broken only by a sand hump
here and there, and tufts of dusty, grey camel-thorn.
In the vivid sunshine each of these tufts threw very
black and sharply defined shadows on the sand. Farther
on, slightly to their left, the ground sloped and they
looked down a shallowish wadi, some fifty feet wide,
dry as a bone, brown, and dotted with small boulders.
Beyond this lay the final approaches to Bardia.

The Sergeant-Major in charge of the platoon was
making his way along a crawl trench to visit his left
section. He had nearly reached them when he was
surprised by the appearance of a strange officer coming
across the desert from the direction of his vehicles. It
was an artillery captain and he seemed to be looking
for somebody.

" Who's in command of this platoon ? " inquired the captain, as the sergeant-major approached.

" I am, sir."

" Oh ! I'm Forward Observation Officer for the 25-pounder battery back on the right. I've just left my vehicle over with yours. Look here, sergeant-major, there's something I'll be very much obliged if you'll do for us."

" What is that, sir ? "

A couple of shells whistled through the air high above their heads. The captain jerked a thumb upwards.

" Put that blasted battery out of business," he said.

The Platoon Sergeant-Major regarded him with barely-concealed astonishment.

" Us, sir ? " he exclaimed. " Why, those guns are somewhere over in Bardia."

" I know that," laughed the F.O.O. " But their eyes aren't. Get your glasses."

They stood side by side with their binoculars to their eyes.

" Top of that crest to the right of the wadi . . ." said the F.O.O. " Come along down the slope to the left . . . Past that big boulder . . . Lower still . . . Between twenty-three and twenty-two hours . . . Got it ? "

The Platoon Sergeant-Major concentrated his gaze on the spot. After a while he distinguished what seemed to be the flat top of a small wooden shed projecting just above the slope about a mile away. The natural colour of the wood made an excellent camouflage against the tawny surroundings.

" What is it, sir ? " asked the Platoon Sergeant-Major.

" The aforesaid eyes," replied the F.O.O. " It's one of those Eye-tie Observation Posts. You know . . . sort of a crow's nest sticking out of the desert on top of a thin tubular steel support like a mast. You can't see the mast from here. It's hidden by the slope of the wadi. But that's the chap that's causing us all the trouble behind. We've got to have him stopped. I'll be very much obliged if you'll send one of your machine-guns forward and do a very useful job."

The Platoon Sergeant-Major did not reply immediately. He came from the North and liked time to bring his canniness to bear upon the unusual. And he regarded this as a most unusual suggestion. He knew what his own orders were, and didn't follow how the F.O.O.'s request fitted in with them.

" I don't see my way to doing that, sir," he demurred, after a pause.

" Why ? "

" Well, it isn't quite our job, sir. We're up here to provide covering fire for the infantry. Our guns are on fixed lines."

" You're not doing anything at the moment," urged the F.O.O.

" But there's no saying what we shall be wanted to do the moment after."

" I quite understand you've got your orders," went on the F.O.O. " But the fact remains. If you can knock out that post you'll be doing the infantry and everyone else a grand turn. I'm sure your company commander would agree with me. I'd go along and find him, only I don't want to waste any time. It's damned urgent to stop that battery's fire for a bit."

" I suppose his own battery is getting it nasty," thought the Platoon Sergeant-Major, as he stood silent while the F.O.O. brought to bear upon him the full extent of his persuasive powers. These were of a very high order and after a time the Platoon Sergeant-Major found himself weakening. He, personally, rather liked the idea of a little relief to the monotony of the afternoon. And certainly, from the way the F.O.O. put things, anything done would be in a good cause. At the same time, like most people, he hated the idea of being persuaded into doing something against his will. So when at last he did give way, it was grudgingly.

" All right . . . We'll have a cut at it, sir," he said

slowly, " but I hope nothing breaks loose while we're doing the job. If so, I'll be held responsible."

" Don't worry. Nothing will happen," said the F.O.O. with the cheerful air of the man who has gained his point. " I'll hang about and watch the result."

Having made his decision the Platoon Sergeant-Major's one object now was to get the business completed as quickly as possible. It had crossed his mind at first to give the crow's nest a few bursts from the nearest section. But almost immediately he washed the idea out. Not much more than the top covering of the platform was visible. Their fire might not be very effective, and the only result would be to give their position away. This was the very last thing he desired.

He walked over to the gun position nearest to the wadi.

" Dismount a gun," he said to the section commander. " I'm going forward down the wadi to shoot up an Eye-tie O.P. It's the bloke that's causing all this noise overhead, and they want it stopped."

" Look out for sniping," observed the corporal. " Plenty of sangars over there where a sniper can hide. I've heard a shot or two."

" I know . . . We'll crawl up along the side of the wadi. There's enough rock there for cover."

" Who will you want ? "

" Few as possible. Detail a No. 1 and No. 2, and I'd better have a range-taker."

" What about the ammo ? "

" Four belts. That should be ample for the job, and leave a bit over for emergencies. We can carry that much between us."

In a short while the little party was making its way gradually towards the mouth of the wadi, picking up what cover they could from low sand humps and patches of camel-thorn. The Platoon Sergeant-Major led the way, carrying one of the wooden boxes that contained 500-rounds of ammunition in a couple of belts. The No. 1 and the loader followed at intervals of a few yards, the latter struggling along under the burden of the other box of ammunition, as well as his 56-lb. tripod. After proceeding half a mile he had nothing good to say regarding the Platoon Sergeant-Major's ideas on economy in men.

At last they reached the entrance to the wadi, which widened gradually in front of them as it led to the flat desert beyond. Cautiously they crept along the foot of the right-hand slope, dodging from boulder to boulder one at a time, and pausing for a few minutes between each move. But no sign of life disturbed them. The whole place seemed utterly deserted except for the lizards sunning themselves on the rocks. Nearing the end of the wadi the Platoon Sergeant-Major signalled a halt while he crept forward alone to reconnoitre. Lying flat on the ground when he reached the end of the slope, the first thing he saw was the Eye-tie O.P., only about 300 yards to his right. The whole contraption was clearly visible. The tubular steel shaft stuck straight up out of the desert like a tall, thin telegraph pole, and he could distinguished the pegs on the sides by which one climbed up to the crow's nest at the top. There seemed to be a low wooden wall round the platform of the latter. He could discern no occupants, so he concluded that whoever might be up there was lying flat on the floor. His eye lingered on the crow's nest ; from where he lay, silhouetted against the clear blue sky.

" What a perfect target," he said to himself. " A real sitter . . . And only three hundred yards range . . ." He felt glad now that he had allowed himself to be over-persuaded by the F.O.O.

He took a look across the desert in front of the wadi. There was no sign of human activity anywhere. He counted about a dozen small sangars spread over a wide area. Some of their low stone walls were not much more than a few yards in circumference. They all appeared to be completely deserted. The nearest was about 500 yards away, except for one that was almost at the foot of the Italian O.P.

Eager to get on with the job, the Platoon Sergeant-Major beckoned the others to come along. They were just mounting the gun when a rifle cracked in the distance. Uttering one solitary sound between a groan and a grunt, the No. 2 collapsed. His body fell across the gun and remained there motionless. He had been shot dead. Automatically, his companions flattened themselves out on the ground and waited for the next. But nothing followed. Everything became quiet again as it had been before. The only difference was that unnaturally inert body hanging over the gun in the sunshine.

"Bloody sniper!" swore the Platoon Sergeant-Major, as soon as he recovered from the shock. He waited a few minutes, and as there was no further shot, he crawled forward and took a look at the body.

"Shot in the back," he said to the others. "Must have come from one of those sangars on the left. Get the gun over to the other side of the wadi. We'll be out of sight from there."

They dragged the body of the dead man behind a boulder without attracting any more attention from the sniper. Then they crept back along the wadi for fifty yards, darted across to the other side, and returned under the shelter of the left-hand slope. From here they had as good a view of the target as before.

"Let's finish off this little job first," said the Platoon Sergeant-Major, grimly.

Which was the first intimation to the rest of them that there was now another on hand. They mounted the gun right opposite the dead body of their companion. The range-taker spread himself out on the ground with his Barr & Stroud to take the range to the O.P.

"Never mind about that," said the Platoon Sergeant-Major. "It's three hundred, near enough. I want you to look out in front and keep those sangars under observation. Let me know the instant you see anything."

The range-taker turned his instrument parallel with the wide strip of desert on which the sangars were dotted.

and glued himself to the eye-piece. The No. 1, with the gun between his legs, sat low on the ground, supporting his back against a small rock. Stretched out at his side the Platoon Sergeant-Major, taking over the job of the dead loader, fed a belt to the gun.

"O.K.," he said. "Range 300 . . . And make it snappy."

The No. 1 gradually lifted the barrel of the gun as he looked along the sight to get an aim on the crow's nest. After a while the gun moved no more. The gunner turned a perplexed face to the Platoon Sergeant-Major.

"What the hell are you waiting for?" said the latter, impatiently. "A blind man would have got in a couple of bursts by now."

"Nothing doing," said the gunner. "Can't get enough elevation on."

The gun was on a low mounting, and they were so close to the target that they couldn't lift it sufficiently to aim at the crow's nest.

"What shall we do?" asked the gunner.

The Platoon Sergeant-Major considered the awkward situation for a few moments. It aggravated him to think of this perfect target, so near and yet so far.

"Think you could hit the upright?" he asked, at length.

"Difficult to lay an aim on it. I'll try."

"With a bit of luck you might be able to saw through it. Give it a long burst . . . Twenty-five."

The gunner nodded, settled his back firmly against the rock, brought the gun down to a low elevation and took careful aim. He lifted his head slightly and looked forward over the top of the sight.

"On . . .!" he exclaimed.

"Fire . . .!" shouted the Platoon Sergeant-Major.

Looking straight ahead at the target, the gunner pressed both thumbs on the thumb-piece, and the silence of the wadi was torn with the rattle of a sustained burst of fire.

At first it seemed they had been unsuccessful. But

just as the gunner was about to press the thumb-piece for a second burst the Platoon Sergeant-Major uttered an exclamation. They saw the long metal pole sway slightly and then topple over. But what astounded them most was to see the bodies of three men suddenly shoot out of the crow's nest as if they had been catapulted from it. Head-foremost, the three executed a graceful curve in the air and fell plumb into the sangar close to the O.P. The sangar had been constructed on a slight slope and part of the interior was visible from the machine-gun position. The Platoon Sergeant-Major ordered the gunner to rake it. Without delay the Number One traversed the whole length of it, backwards and forwards, tapping the traversing handles right and left, sending over bursts of twenty-five between each tap. Chips of stone from the walls of the sangar flew about in all directions.

After a thorough traverse they ceased firing and waited a minute or so for the dust to settle. But within the sangar there was no sign of any movement.

"Needn't waste any more on that," said the Platoon Sergeant-Major contentedly. "I never saw anything like the way those fellows shot off that platform. Like a high-diving show at Blackpool."

He contemplated what had been the O.P. The wooden crow's nest lay smashed on the ground, and about six feet of the tubular steel support remained sticking up out of the desert like a truncated sapling.

"You may have had a bit of luck," he said to the gunner. "But there's no denying that was damn good shooting."

The gunner grinned. "Do we pack up now?" he asked.

"Not quite," replied the Platoon Sergeant-Major, his glance travelling across the wadi to where the body of the loader lay. He frowned heavily, and turned his head towards the range-taker.

"Spotted anything yet?" he asked.

Flat on his stomach to the left of the gun, the range-taker was still keeping the desert in front under observation. His Barr & Stroud gave him a wide range of vision, bringing all the sangars into the picture. There was not much chance of anything escaping his eye with an instrument that magnified thirteen times, far more powerful than field-glasses. He hadn't moved from the eye-piece for a second ; not even to see what had been the fate of the crow's nest.

The Platoon Sergeant-Major had barely spoken when the range-taker shouted :

" Think I've got something . . ."

" Where ? "

" Second sangar on the far left. . . . Six-fifty yards."

The Platoon Sergeant-Major instantly crept round to the rear of the gun.

" You look after the belt," he said to the gunner. " This one belongs to me," he added grimly.

They exchanged places and the Platoon Sergeant-Major traversed the gun on to the distant sangar.

After a few seconds the range-taker launched into a running commentary :

" I can see someone moving now . . .

" He's crawling along . . .

" I think he's going to come out from the left end . . .

" He's stopped now . . .

" If you lay your sights on the left end I'll give you the tip when to fire . . ."

There was a brief pause. No one else spoke. The Platoon Sergeant-Major carefully laid the gun as directed. Then the range-taker began again :

" He's going to move now . . .

" He's getting up . . .

" He'll be out soon . . .

" He's close to the end . . .

" He's stopped . . .

" He's moving . . .

" Ready, now . . .

" Ready . . .

" Fire . . ."

At the same moment the Platoon Sergeant-Major pressed on the thumb-piece. Once more the slopes of the wadi echoed with the sharp rattle of the machine-gun. A burst of twenty-five sped through the air towards the left end of the sangar. Another followed almost immediately.

" O.K.," announced the range-taker calmly. " He's down for keeps."

He withdrew his forehead from the Barr & Stroud, blinking a bit in the strong sunlight. His eyes were strained with their prolonged vigil, and he rubbed them with his knuckles for relief. The Platoon Sergeant-Major was completing the job by spraying all the sangars he could see in the area.

" That's made me feel good again," he announced when he had finished. " We'll get back now, as quickly as possible. Likely enough we've attracted some attention."

They began to pack up hurriedly.

" What are we going to do about him ? " asked the range-taker, nodding towards the dead loader.

" Have to leave him," said the Platoon Sergeant-Major. " We've got all we can manage to carry as it is. I'll send out and get him to-night. I know the C.S.M. will like to have him for his own little cemetery. This'll make five."

" Shall I take his disc and pay-book ? "

" Better not, as we'll be bringing him in later."

The dead man had been wearing his greatcoat, and the Platoon Sergeant-Major walked across and turned up the ends of it over his head as a protection against the flies. The loader was the first man he had had killed in his platoon, and though he wasn't sentimental and knew full well that war couldn't be conducted without casualties, nevertheless he felt a personal resentment.

" Anyhow, I'm bloody glad we've been able to leave him a bit of company," he remarked, looking with satisfaction over the desert towards the sangar beside which the sniper lay riddled with bullets.

III—Conversion in the Wadi

Zero hour was eleven a.m. It was now half-past ten.
The two companies of Australian infantry detailed for
the attack were taking it easy half-way up the deep,
narrow wadi that narrowed further as it led to the top
of the escarpment. About three hundred yards farther
up, the wadi was crossed, right and left, by a track
which at the bottom passed over a low stone bridge.
This track was their datum line.

It was an overcast morning, and cold. Wrapped in
their greatcoats the infantrymen lay dispersed in twos
and threes among such scanty cover as the small boulders
and camel-thorn tufts on the right slope of the wadi
provided. Fairly persistent shelling was going on from
the enemy heavy guns away on the escarpment to their
right. Occasionally, too, a few machine-gun bullets
whistled through the air, coming from indeterminate
directions. Neither worried the waiting infantry in the
slightest. Clinging to the right side of the wadi they
watched, when they troubled to look, the shells sailing
over their heads to explode out of sight on the other side.

A long, leathery-faced Australian with very pale blue
eyes, and his tin hat at an angle of forty-five degrees,
sauntered across to a nearby boulder and dropped beside
the soldier who was sitting with his back propped up
against it.

" Got the makings, Leslie ? " he asked.

" Help yourself, Steve," replied the other, handing him
a flat tobacco tin. He was a good-looking youth, with
a cheerful and rather innocent expression, and was otherwise distinguished from his companion by the fact that
he had more recently shaved.

Steve rolled himself a cigarette with the deft fingers of
an artist.

" Listen to this, Les," he began. " And then tell me what you think of them pommy friends of yours now."

" What, again ? " laughed Leslie.

" Yes, again. And again after that," sneered Steve. " I'm not prejudiced by having an English aunt like you."

With a tolerant smile Leslie resigned himself to a further instalment of the eternal argument. It wasn't, in fact, an argument so much as a diatribe delivered by Steve in serial parts, whenever anything happened to give him a fresh start. It had begun in the cantonments outside Alexandria when they first chummed up, not long after their arrival in Egypt. In civil life Steve was a stockman on a sheep station in the Riverina. He liked to proclaim himself a hundred-and-one per cent Australian. As principal proof of this he cherished a sublime contempt for the entire race of English or, to use his own favourite designation, " pommy bastards." He refused to admit them one saving grace. His personal knowledge of them was not large. It included a few encounters with some rather indifferent specimens on the Riverina. On this he based his withering judgments of the whole tribe. What he lacked in knowledge he made up in consistency. Nothing that was English could be any good.

It was his chief exasperation that he could never get his pal Leslie to agree with him. Steve attributed the amusement with which Leslie received his continual instances of pommy inferiority to the fact that he possessed an English aunt who lived at Hammersmith, and from time to time sent her nephew a letter. Steve considered that although Leslie had never seen this distant relative, nevertheless the possession of her gave him a deplorable bias in favour of England and things English. He was sorry about this, because in all other ways Leslie was a very nice, sensible fellow.

" You'd think just the same as I do, Les, if it wasn't for that English aunt of yours you've never seen," Steve would say.

"No, I wouldn't," Leslie replied good-humouredly. "Nor would I just because I'd met a few pommy dopes in the Riverina. I got more sense than that."

He had, indeed, a much wider knowledge of English types than Steve. He came from Sydney where, before the war broke out, he drove a lorry for one of those big pastoral concerns that look after all the stockman's wants, from the cradle to the grave. In the course of his brief life he had met many pommies, good, bad and indifferent—just as he had met good, bad and indifferent Australians. More to the point, however, was the freedom of his mind from any trace of bigotry. It rendered him slow to accumulate prejudices.

Naturally, in those first days in Egypt, Steve turned his cold, blue, disdainful eye upon the British soldier. In particular, he derided their discipline, which contrasted strongly with the more free-and-easy methods of the Australians.

"All pretty Fanny!" he jeered. "What I want to know is, are they fighting men?"

"You don't want to know, Steve. You've made up your mind already," replied Leslie.

"They got to show me first."

"Ain't we got to show them, too?"

"Les, you're not putting us in the same class as these pommies," exclaimed Steve with genuine pain. "We're born fighters. We don't have to be drilled into it like these blokes. What would we want with all this parade-ground stuff? It's just the bullsh. You're a born fighter, or you're not. That makes sense, don't it?"

"Sure."

"Then why?"

"Why what?"

"Why argue?"

"I ain't arguing. I'm listening," said Leslie.

"All this fancy drill and discipline, and spit-and-polish, what does it amount to?" pursued Steve. "Just show stuff. Makes good-looking peace-time soldiers for pro-cessions and the Aldershot Tattoo. But it don't give

a man fighting guts. That's what wins battles. And
that's what we'll show these pommy bastards. No, Les,
I ain't got much use for them."

" Those I've spoken to seem nice, friendly blokes,"
observed Leslie.

" And why not ? " demanded Steve. " Ain't we come
a long way to show 'em how to do the job ? "

He paused for a moment in search of some new point
of criticism.

" And look at them battle-blouses they wear ? " he
added. " What's wrong with tunics, like us ? Why do
they do it ? Ain't they cissy-looking enough ? "

At which Leslie burst into loud laughter.

" Come on, you horny old bushman," he cried. " Time
I bought you a drink."

This may be taken as a sample of many similar con-
versations between the two friends before the Wavell
push into Libya began. And now, this morning, for
the first time in the campaign, the Australians were
going into action supported by English troops in the
shape of a machine-gun platoon, whose trucks were
waiting in readiness some distance down the wadi.

Steve lit his cigarette and hung it on his bottom lip.

" Get it off your chest," said Leslie with a smile.
" What have the pommies done now ? You ain't said
anything about them for four days."

Steve ejected a couple of jets of smoke from his nostrils.

" You know them tanks that were to go in with us
when we put in the attack," he began.

Leslie nodded.

" Well, they've called it off."

This, if true, was indeed a bit of news. It stirred
Leslie to interest.

" Why ? " he inquired.

" Don't ask me, Digger," replied Steve, conscious of
having made an impression. " All I know is that quarter
of an hour ago up comes one of them spick-and-span
pommy majors in a truck to Battalion H.Q. He shakes
hands with the Colonel, gives him the how-d'ye-do, all

very polite and gentlemanly, and says : ' Fearfully, awf'ly sorry, old chap, and all that sort of thing. But I'm afraid you'll have to do without our invaluable assistance to-day. Confounded nuisance, of course, and all that sort of thing. Very sincere apologies for any inconvenience it will cause you. Wouldn't have had it happen for worlds.' And any amount more of that polite bullsh," added Steve.

" What's the reason ? " asked Leslie.

Steve spat viciously.

" Reason ! " he exclaimed. " To hell with reasons ! You bet, those pommy bastards have got hundreds of 'em. All nice, polite ones. The fact remains. The tanks won't be there. And we shall. Now, ain't that as I've always said it'd be ? Just forget your English aunt for once, Les."

Leslie regarded his comrade for a moment or two in silence. A sceptical smile appeared round the corners of his mouth.

" What did the Colonel say when he heard ? " he asked innocently.

" He just turned to the other officers present and said : ' Gentlemen, we have got to be very sorry for this here pommy major and his pals. They won't have the honour of accompanying us in the attack this morning.' After that the pommy major got in his truck and went off."

Leslie stretched himself back against the boulder with a shout of delighted laughter.

" You bloody old liar," he exclaimed admiringly. " Now I'll tell you something. How do you come to know all this when you've been lying out here on the ground alongside of me for the past half-hour or more ? "

" Dinkum oil," Steve protested, hurt. " Gawd's trewth, as your pommy pals would say."

" How do you know ? " insisted Leslie.

Steve assumed the air of mysterious sources of knowledge.

" Digger, make no mistake. I've got my ear to the ground," he replied.

" It's full of sand," said Leslie.

Nevertheless, Steve was not entirely wrong, though his travesty of the interview between the tank major and the Australian C.O. was everything that Leslie considered it to be. It was a fact that the tanks would not be taking part in the attack. The squadron had been in action all the previous day and had been knocked about a bit. Both the Squadron Commander and the Second-in-Command were badly wounded. In addition, they had not yet been able to replenish their exhausted fuel supplies. And this was the deciding factor.

Any further discussion on the matter between the two friends was cut short by the sound of a whistle.

" We're off," said Steve, gathering himself up.

From all over the slope of the wadi men jumped to to their feet and commenced to walk forward in extended order, their rifles before them at the " Ready." They advanced in thin waves. The platoon to which Leslie and Steve belonged was in the second. At precisely eleven o'clock the first line of infantrymen crossed the track across the wadi. After which they proceeded to move forward up the trough of the wadi at a slightly faster speed. Enemy shells continued to pass over them and burst on the far side of the escarpment. Stray machine-gun bullets whizzed down the wadi. But there was nothing to hinder their progress. They pressed on steadily without a casualty, and at last emerged on to the wide, flat plateau at the neck of the wadi. Here all seemed peaceful enough. There was no sign of any enemy, and the men fanned out and continued to stride briskly forward over the dusty, stony ground.

They had traversed about two hundred yards of the plateau when without warning the roar of guns sounded from in front of them to their left. They had no time to realise what had happened before the shells began to burst in their midst.

" My earth . . . ! " shouted Steve, as he flung himself on the ground beside Leslie, and crawled for shelter to a low rock. " What's hit us ? "

All over the plateau the rest of the troops were hurriedly

engaged in seeking cover. But this was not easy. The plateau was bare and wide-open to the sky. It was level and featureless, with here and there a few small grey boulders, round which the wind had collected the sand in little heaps. Upon this exposed position, practically shelterless, the unfortunate infantrymen were at the mercy of the rain of shells that continued to fall among them. Every few seconds the earth went up in an explosion. The whole plateau sprouted mushroom growths of smoke and dust and stones. Dead and wounded dotted the ground. Men scraped frantically to hollow out depressions in the sand, and built up small piles of stones, behind which they flattened themselves as close to the ground as possible. After the first surprise the rattle of their own rifle fire sounded amid the concussion of the shells.

The Company Commander had run up to find out the cause of the hold-up. He was crouched beside Steve's Platoon Officer, who was surveying the front through his binoculars.

" It's that fort on the left," announced the latter finally. " About eight hundred yards, I should think. I calculate they've got about ten field-guns there, from all the fuss they're kicking up."

" What the hell's gone wrong ! " shouted the Company Commander furiously. " That fort was marked on the map as deserted."

He pulled out his map-case to make sure he had not been mistaken.

" There it is," he said. " Deserted."

" It's inhabited all right now," said the Platoon Officer grimly. " They'll simply blow us off the plateau."

" Runner ! . . ." shouted the Company Commander, and looking round for the nearest man, his eye alighted on Steve.

" Get back like hell to the machine-gun platoon, and tell 'em we're held up," he ordered.

Steve sped back in the direction of the wadi. He

hadn't gone far when a shell burst so close that the blast blew him off his feet. He gathered himself together again and ran on. A little farther on he encountered the Intelligence Officer, who was hurrying up from B.H.Q. to see what the trouble was. The I.O. was crossing over to speak to him when another shell burst a short distance away. A fragment hit the officer in the chest, spun him round like a teetotum, and spread him on the ground. Steve glanced at him, hesitated a moment, and then ran on. His mission was too urgent for any delay.

The machine-gunners, with their four trucks, were parked in the bed of the wadi, half-way down. Steve halted in front of the Platoon Commander, a lieutenant with just that air of neatness and finish about him that never failed to stimulate his pommy prejudices. He delivered his message. Almost before he had finished the lieutenant had shouted to the two senior sergeants of the platoon. They joined him, with a range-taker and an orderly to act as runner, and in a few seconds the little group were hastening up the wadi with Steve panting beside them.

" What's the opposition ? " inquired the lieutenant.

" I heard my Platoon Commander say it was one of them stone forts," replied Steve. " The Captain had it marked on his map as deserted. They waited till we'd got right out in the open, and then let fly at us from about eight hundred yards with ten field-guns. That's my Platoon Commander's estimate."

" Nasty surprise," commented the lieutenant.

His easy, casual tone irritated Steve. " There you are," he thought. " A typical fancy sort of pommy remark. Mustn't forget he's a gentleman. All right, you machine-gun bastards. You wait until you get out on the plain. You won't feel so la-di-da then, I bet."

They emerged from the neck of the wadi on to the shell-swept plateau. In the interval of Steve's absence there had been no diminution in the deadliness of the artillery fire. Already the Australians had lost nearly one-fifth of their men in dead and wounded. One of the companies had been withdrawn and was now toiling up the left slope of the wadi to the escarpment above, with the intention of attacking the fort from the rear. The result of this diversion was problematical, and in any case would not bring immediate relief.

" Where's your Company Commander ? " the lieutenant asked Steve.

Steve led the way to the spot where the infantry captain awaited them with a harassed look on his face. The two officers held a brief consultation.

" Fort on the left," shouted the lieutenant to the range-taker. " See what it is."

He turned to the runner and gave him some orders in a crisp, matter-of-fact tone. The man ran back to the N.C.O. who had been left in charge of the trucks in the wadi.

Meanwhile the range-taker had set up his Barr & Stroud, and was lying flat on the ground behind it, glued to the eyepieces.

" Seven-Five-O yards, sir," he announced without looking up.

From his precarious shelter behind a small boulder close by, Steve watched these preliminaries with a disdainful interest. He glanced round for Leslie. He just wanted to tell him once more what he thought of the " pommy bastards." But Leslie was not to be seen where Steve had left him.

" Surely the bloody fool hasn't been trying to push forward in face of all this," he thought. " Be just like him."

His concern over his friend was almost immediately diverted by the arrival of a machine-gun section, and as if to signalise their advent, the enemy guns dropped a couple of shells right in their path, and not very many yards ahead. The air was momentarily clouded by flying lumps of earth, stones, fumes, and hissing shell splinters.

" Now we shall see . . ." thought Steve grimly.

But what he saw when the disturbance had subsided was the machine-gun section still advancing into action with that drill-like order and coolness which had so often been the subject of his ridicule. The Number Ones of the guns carried, in regulation style, the tripods and dial sights. The Number Twos stooping slightly under the weight, carried the guns, low down at the full length of their arms, and the spare-parts case. Behind came the men with the condenser-cases containing water for cooling the Vickers, and a couple of belt-boxes in addition. Four more ammunition numbers, two for each gun, and carrying more belt-boxes, completed the party. In spite of himself, Steve began to feel slightly impressed by this imperturbable little procession. He forgot Leslie, for the time being, and settled down to watch proceedings.

He saw the senior section commander give the signal " Action " by extending his hands from the body and waving them in a circle. The two gun crews crawled forward with their gear. The guns were mounted on their low tripods, fifteen yards apart. Each Number One sat behind his gun with his legs outstretched. His loader lay on the ground, on his right, and passed the tag of a belt of ammunition through the feed-block.

" All . . . Seven-Five-O. . . . Left of arc. . . . Large brown fort . . ." shouted the Platoon Commander.

The Number Ones peered along the sights, elevating and depressing and traversing the gun as required. After a few moments they raised their heads and looked steadily in front of them over the top of their guns in the direction of the target. With their forefingers they lifted the safety catches, and simultaneously their thumbs hovered on the thumb-pieces of the guns.

" On . . ." they informed their leaders.

Steve heard the loader of the gun nearest to him say to his Number One : " Give 'em a bloody good burst to begin with." He saw the loader extend his arm from behind his back, to signal they were ready.

On the flank the neat and well-clipped-looking Platoon Commander was standing up calmly among the flying shell fragments, his glasses dangling from his neck. He raised the flat palm of his hand, paused for a second and then dropped it abruptly. It was the signal to fire. The loaders, watching, tapped their Number Ones on the back. A loud, sharp, and continuous burr-r-r filled the air as the machine-guns despatched their opening burst. A hundred rounds to begin with, so as to see clearly where the bullets were striking.

The Platoon Commander lifted his glasses. Close by, the range-taker lay stretched on the ground peering through his Barr & Stroud, to check the range.

" All . . . down Five-O . . ." shouted the Platoon Commander.

The Number Ones readjusted their range, looked along their sights and then stared steadily forward again. Once more the Platoon Officer raised the open palm of his hand and dropped it abruptly. Once more the vicious burr-r-r echoed across the plateau. All as cool, precise and unruffled as if at target practice.

Watching the machine-gunners, Steve found his interest gradually deepen into admiration. At first it was a grudging admiration, and he struggled to check it. As a hundred-and-one per cent. Australian it made him feel uncomfortable to find himself thinking well of pommies. But as the minutes passed his resistance grew fainter.

The Number One of the gun nearest to him tapped the traversing handles, first right, then left, in order to sweep his target.

The ammunition numbers, crouched a few yards behind, ran forward at intervals with fresh belt-boxes, and then ran back to their places again.

After some time the sergeant at the firing-point stretched out his right arm from the shoulder, and the ammunition numbers rose as one man and doubled back to the trucks to bring up new supplies of belt-boxes.

Steve passed from admiration to fascination. He wasn't fool enough not to recognise a good thing when he saw it. As the machine-gunners continued to send off burst after burst, he began to feel that they had taken complete charge of affairs as, indeed, they temporarily had. More than this, he felt quite satisfied that this should be so. There was something about the way these pommies were handling things that inspired him with confidence. Everything moved as on oiled wheels. They allowed nothing to disturb them. They knew what they were about. As for the shell-fire, it might just as well not have been there. They continued making their little signals, and flicking their traversing handles to right and left as if it never existed. Steve chuckled appreciatively. " Good old pommy bastards," he said to himself. " I would't have believed it."

The unhesitating precision of their methods gripped him. Instinctively he felt the deadly efficiency behind it all. Men and gun functioning together like parts of some well-ordered, ruthless machine that nothing could stop. . . .

" It's a grand show," he murmured.

The efficiency of the machine-gunners was by now producing visible effects. Much to the satisfaction of the hard-tried infantry, the fire from the fort began to die down. Fewer shells burst on the plateau, and after a while the enemy guns were silenced completely. The machine-gunners put in a last strong burst or two to clinch matters.

Almost before the shell-fire had died away the Australians were on their feet, making for the fort. Steve ran forward with them. The last thing he saw was the neat, trim Platoon Commander signalling " Cease fire," and the machine-gun crews unloading and collecting their kit, with the same drill-book orthodoxy that had characterised them throughout the action. This time the sight of the neat, trim, unmistakably pommy-looking Platoon Commander did not irritate him in the least.

As Steve hurried forward he was thinking that he would have something to tell Leslie when he saw him. Les would probably ride him a bit. But he didn't mind admitting when he'd made a mistake. Everybody was liable to. . . . He went on, keeping his eyes open for Leslie.

He found him at last. Leslie was lying on his back, with his eyes wide-open, staring at the sky.

" Les ! . . . Les ! . . . What's happened to you ? " cried Steve in dismay.

He bent down and gently raised his comrade's head.

" Les ! . . . Digger ! . . ." he shouted again.

There was no reply. Leslie's dead face looked at him in silence, with that faint, sceptical lift of the lips that he knew so well.

For a second or two Steve remained with his friend's head on his arm. Then he lowered it to the ground. He jumped to his feet and raced towards the fort, rage in his heart.

*   *   *   *   *   *

Several weeks later a mild-faced, elderly spinster lady was taking tea in her Hammersmith flat with a neighbour. She was talking about her nephew, news of whose death in the Middle East she had just received.

" He was my youngest sister's boy. The one who died in Sydney four years ago," she said. " I never saw him. But I used to write to him. Such a fine young fellow, he was. Look . . ."

And she produced a photograph of Leslie, aged six, as testimony. A tear trickled down the side of her thin nose.

" It is hard," murmured the neighbour sympathetically. " What did the War Office say ? "

" Oh, my dear, I didn't hear from the War Office. Leslie's nothing to do with the War Office. He's an Australian," said the spinster aunt proudly. " It was a boy named Steve who wrote to me. He says he was Leslie's friend. I must say I can't quite make head or tail of his letter. He doesn't write too well. There's a lot about some English machine-gunners. What they were doing mixed up with the Australians I can't imagine. . . . He says he had something he wanted to tell Leslie, and as he can't, he'd like to tell me instead. But he writes in such a confused way. . . . It's something about our English soldiers. He says, as far as I can make out, he wants to let me know that they are grand . . . as

good as Australians. . . . Fancy thinking I needed to
be told that our boys are grand ! . . . He must be a
very peculiar young man. . . ."

IV—Bearing, One–One–O

HEAD and shoulders projecting from the turret of his
tank, the Squadron Commander pushed his goggles up
on to his forehead and swept the desert horizon with his
glasses.   There was nothing to be seen except the miles
upon miles of brown and white pebbly desert, dotted
with low tufts of camel thorn, resembling a poor sort of
heather, and covered with yellow dust.   Whether he
stared to his left, right, or in front of him the same
monotonous, dirty, brown waste filled his binoculars—
flat featureless, lifeless.   Above, the clear, hard, blue
sky appeared equally flat, featureless and lifeless.   But
he was not quarrelling with that.

He lowered his glasses and glanced behind where the
other eight tanks of the squadron lumbered in his rear
along the desert road, at a distance of fifty yards from
each other.   Not much more was visible to him than the
thick, swirling dust cloud they churned up from the
powdery surface of the track.

Some men are oppressed by a sense of their utter
insignificance, sandwiched between the vast expanses of
the desert and the tremendous vault of its cloudless
sky.   Not so the Squadron Commander.   By some
curious psychological freak the very emptiness of the
desert made him feel acutely conscious of being terribly
conspicuous.   Try as he would, he was unable to rid
himself of this uncomfortable illusion.   It afflicted him
disagreeably whenever he was on the move in daylight.
He attributed it to the sudden and severe bombing
attack he had undergone the very first time he went
out into the desert on patrol in the days that preceded

Graziani's advance on Sollum.   He knew it was ridiculous.
But it clung.   And one effect was to make him harbour
a grudge against his own dust.   That being about as
sane as a man's falling out with his own shadow, he kept
his idiosyncrasy strictly private.   Watching the significant
cloud flung up now by his squadron, he said to himself :
   " I shan't be sorry when it's time to halt.   If there's
an Eye-tie up aloft, he can't possibly miss that."
   The squadron of Hussars, consisting of nine five-ton
tanks armed only with Vickers machine-guns, were
moving up the road from Mekili to Derna.   Tobruk had
been captured by the British, but Derna was still in
the possession of the Italians, though they were soon
to be driven out of it by the Australian infantry at the
point of the bayonet.   Meanwhile, an armoured division
had struck south across the desert to Mekili to prepare
for an advance that would cut off any possible Italian
retreat from Benghazi.   It was still on the cards that
the Italians might venture a move on Mekili from Derna,
and the squadron of Hussars was under orders to proceed
northwards for several miles up the road to cover it in
the event of an attack.
   As they advanced the yellow dust-cloud thickened,
smothering the tanks, till, despite the brilliant sunshine,
each driver could discern little beyond the unwieldly
shadow of the vehicle in front of him lumbering along
in a pea-soup fog.
   " As a road it may have its advantages," reflected the
Squadron Commander, " but as a dust-pan it's got the
trackless desert beaten to a frazzle."
   And he registered thanks that there was practically no
breeze to send their footprints whirling high into the sky.
   At last, about fifteen miles from Mekili, he brought
the squadron to a halt.   The crew commanders came
running up.
   " 2-Troop and 3-Troop move off the road to the right.
1-Troop to the left," he ordered.
   The squadron deployed into the desert some distance
from each side of the road, and settled down to await

whatever the far-distant horizon had in store for them. Crew commanders and drivers took the opportunity of stretching their legs, and as the morning wore on and the sun grew hotter they began to divest themselves, piece by piece, of the clothing they had piled on to protect them from the bitter cold at night.   After a couple of hours most of them were content with their shirts and shorts.

Another half-hour passed.   Tired of watching his driver chase scorpions in and out of the small rocks near his tank with a forked stick, the Squadron Commander took another sweep of the horizon with his glasses.   He was quite prepared to see what he had seen on each of many similar sweeps during the past two and half-hours ;—the desert, tawny in the strong sunlight with each little rock and camel-thorn throwing its sharp shadow ;   the desert, disappearing in a level monotony to meet the straight line of the blue, metallic sky, God knows how many miles away ;   the desert, vast, empty, expressionless, and lifeless.

However, this time it seemed to him there was a difference.   It was sufficient to cause him to clamber on the top of his tank for a better field of vision.   As he did so he noticed 2-Troop Commander near to his left, engaged in a similar operation.

For nearly a minute the Squadron Commander stood upright on the roof of his tank, his glasses fixed steadily at the same spot on the horizon.   Then he jumped down and strode across to 2-Troop Commander.

" What do you make of it ? " he asked.

" Dust, sir," was the reply.   " It's getting taller."

" Means it's coming our way," said the Squadron Commander, climbing up beside the other.   " Wonder what it's going to be."

" Armoured cars. . . . Infantry in trucks, perhaps," suggested the Troop Commander hopefully.

" You're only a blatant optimist," laughed the Squadron Commander.   He took another long look at the distant sky-line.   " Whatever it is, there's a lot of it," he said. " They're kicking up a tremendous amount of dirt."

He slipped down within the turret of the tank and grabbed the microphone of the Troop Commander's wireless.

" Prepare for action ! " he shouted. " Enemy approaching. . . . Can't say what they are yet. . . ."

While the rest of the squadron got into fighting trim the Squadron Commander rejoined his companion on the top of the tank. From now on they watched the approaching dust-cloud in silence, gripped by the suspense of the pause before revelation. The great hush of the desert around them seemed to intensify the exciting potentialities of each moment. Ten minutes passed. Not a word had been spoken.

Suddenly the dust cloud yielded its secret. The Squadron Commander sucked in his breath. A number of dark olive-green shapes began to grow very prominent against the fawn background of the desert. But what interested him most was the nature of those shapes. He took one final look to make sure.

" Medium tanks," he said softly, lowering his glasses.

" Eleven of them," added the Troop Commander. " We're going to be in the way here, sir. They mount 2-pounders, and we've nothing but our Vickers."

The Squadron Commander regarded him thoughtfully for a moment or two.

" Quite right," he said. " It's time to say ' Good-bye.' But I've an idea we'll make it one of those railway-station farewells. You know, long-drawn-out affairs."

He slipped into the turret again and held the microphone to his lips.

" Enemy medium tanks approaching," he shouted. " M.13's. . . . We can't engage. . . . Wait till we hear from them . . . then follow me. . . ."

Emerging once more on to the top of the tank he saw the Italian tanks deploy into battle-line about a couple of miles away and move towards them at a speed of ten miles an hour. A couple of bright flashes leapt from the centre of the line, and a couple of 2-pounder shells kicked up the dust well in front of the squadron.

" Good enough," chuckled the Squadron Commander. " They know we're here."

He raced across to his own tank, dropped through the turret, seized the oil-stained map, and studied it attentively with regard to the position of Mekili. In a few quick seconds he had marked out a course striking across the desert well to the south-east of Mekili. Through the open turret he heard the echo of another 2-pounder on the left of the Italian line. He nodded approvingly, and went on taking a compass bearing of his new course. Now it was time to be off.

" Advance . . ." he ordered his driver. " Right . . . Right . . . Right . . . Steady . . ."

These orders brought him on his new course that would draw the enemy across the desert away from Mekili, and after telling the driver to keep the speed at ten miles an hour, which was sufficient to maintain their present distance from the enemy line, he popped his head out of the turret and saw with satisfaction the rest of the squadron moving abreast of him on a front of nearly half a mile. Behind, on a wider front, the Italian tanks were sweeping after them in a long billow of yellow dust, not more than twelve hundred yards away. But the Squadron Commander was quite content. He knew they wouldn't be able to cut down that distance.

They were using every ounce of their speed. At any time he liked he could show them a clean pair of heels. But he had other intentions, and the thought of these filled him with glee. He would lure the Italians on and on into the trackless desert, always keeping just out of range. But not too far, lest their persistence might flag. Close enough to keep the bait tempting. He'd have their mouths watering all the time. And sooner or later they'd get their feast. Of the precise time and nature of this feast he could not be certain. But he had the utmost confidence that it would be a hearty one when it was dished up.

Having checked up his bearing once again, he switched over his wireless set to transmit, and spoke in cool, precise tones into the microphone.

" Bolo to Kata. . . . . Bolo to Kata. . . . . I have message for you. . . . Over. . . ."

" Bolo " was his squadron's call sign.   " Kata " the call sign of the Division H.Q., some thirty miles to the east of Mekili.

He hadn't long to wait for the reply.

" Kata answering. . . . . Pass your message. . . . . Over. . . ."

The Squadron Commander switched again to transmit.

" Contacted eleven Italian M.13 tanks on Mekili-Derna road," he said.   " Ten miles north of Mekili. . . . Am proceeding on bearing of One-One-O degrees. . . . Speed One-O miles an hour. . . . Enemy following. . . . Bolo to Kata. . . . Over. . . ."

The message was repeated back to him.   " Correct," he said, switched over to receive, and sat back to await the next call with more than a mild curiosity as to its likely nature.   It came after five minutes.

" Keep same course same speed."   That was all.

" Certainly not informative," the Squadron Commander laughed.   " I'll see how things are going outside."

He thrust his head out of the turret.   Nothing much had altered.   His own squadron was moving steadily forward across the desert, with the Italian tanks in pursuit firing an occasional shell into the dust cloud they left in their wake.   After a while the Squadron Commander came to the conclusion that these shells were falling too far behind.

" Mustn't let them get downhearted," he thought, with a grin.   He shouted to the driver :

" Slow. . . . Steady. . . ."   And the squadron proceeded at a slightly reduced speed, which flattered their pursuers into thinking they were overtaking them.   After a few minutes the 2-pounders became quite busy.

" Good ! "   exclaimed   the   Squadron   Commander. " They're getting hot again."

In this way, with alternate variations in speed on the part of the squadron, and keeping his average of ten miles an hour, the chase continued for three-quarters of an hour, and the Squadron Commander enjoyed every minute of it.   Now and again he recalled the laconic message from Division.   Whatever it might mean, he felt in no particular hurry for the elucidation.   No point in spoiling a fine bit of fun too soon.

His exuberance seemed too rich not to share with the other fellows.   He picked up the microphone.

" Grand sport, isn't it ? " he said.   " Mouse plays with cat, for a change. . . . I've just been through to Kata. . . . Oh, oh, Antonio. . . . "

" They'll guess all right what that means," he chuckled.

The dust that had collected in his throat while he was looking out of the turret, together with the heat of the sun and the excitement of being hunted with the pack in full view, engendered a sudden and implacable thirst.   Unscrewing his Thermos, he swallowed a couple of mouthfuls of tea, and wondered if he were merely shifting the grit from his throat or taking on board a new consignment.

" Beats me how this damn sand finds its way into everything," he murmured, for the ten-thousandth time since the campaign started.   And tapping his driver on the back with his foot, he handed him down a drink.

With earphones still on and goggles clinging to the edge of his beret, he turned his cupola around again to see how things were going.   Fine. . . . Just as he would have wished.   A nice bit of desert separated his squadron from the pursuing tanks.   Enough and not too much. " Keep it steady . . ." he shouted to the driver.   As he spoke the red flash of another 2-pounder appeared in his orbit.   The shell fell away to his left, a hundred yards short, and almost immediately there were three more flashes on his right."

" Getting impatient," he laughed.

But the laugh broke off abruptly.   A voice sounded in the earphones.

49   D

" Bolo speaking. . . . Running short of petrol. . . .
Only enough for another seven miles. . . ."

The Squadron Commander could hardly believe his
ears. It was incredible. Then, added to his disbelief,
came a deep resentment against the discord that had
obtruded itself upon his pleasant frame of mind.

" Don't be funny," he replied tartly. " Have another
look. . . . A good one. . . ."

" Sheer bloody nonsense," he muttered irritably.

But he was left with a very uncomfortable impression
which caused him to shout down to his driver :

" How's the petrol ? "

" Running low, sir," was the reply.

" What the hell does this mean ? " the Squadron
Commander exclaimed angrily. " Didn't you fill up ? "

" Moved off before we had a chance, sir. Supply hadn't
arrived."

" Then why the devil wasn't I told ? "

The driver hadn't any light to throw on the subject.
But that did not matter now. The Squadron Commander
was receiving all the enlightenment he could wish for
through his earphones, as one after another his tanks
came through to report petrol shortage. None of them
had more than half-an-hour's supply, and some barely that.

" A damn fine mess we're in now," he exclaimed, with
a bitterness that summed up all his disgust at the dramatic
turn of affairs. " Unless we get help pretty soon, we'll
be nabbed."

He grabbed the microphone and got through to Division
H.Q.

" Petrol running out. . . . Only half-hour's supply
. . . " he reported.

This time he awaited the reply with an anxiety that
had been completely absent on the previous occasion.
His impatience made the interval seem interminable,
though it was only a few minutes. Then the message
came :

" Keep same course same speed . . ."

No more and no less than before. In the Squadron

Commander's present mood he found the repetition highly unsatisfactory.

" All bloody fine," he commented, cursing vigorously. " But for how long. . . ."

There was nothing else to do but to carry on. No use trying to hoard petrol. If they moved slower, they'd get caught. If they speeded up, they'd upset Division's plans—whatever they might be. Why the devil couldn't they have given him just a hint? Did they think, sitting away there comfortably on their backsides, that it was fun being chased about the desert with no petrol by a lot of M.13's?

The fact that only a few minutes previously he had been enjoying the fun was completely forgotten. Which is always the way when a joke turns sour.

Five more precious minutes passed. The Squadron Commander, with his eyes glued to the slits, turned the cupola from right to left along the far horizon facing him, but saw nothing to bring him comfort. At last, in his growing suspense, the restricted field of vision got on his nerves. So he thrust his head right out of the turret, regardless of the dust that soon plastered his face, and through which the sweat trickled down in little channels. The squadron was still moving abreast of him at a steady pace, with the Italian tanks still the same distance to the rear. Their 2-pounders were flashing more frequently now. Though the shells dropped harmlessly they produced, in the present circumstances, a gloomy effect on the Squadron Commander when he thought of the feeble reply their own Vickers' would make when it came to the show-down. Yes, there was no dodging it. They'd be wiped out if help didn't arrive soon. . . .

He found himself repeating over again Division's message : " Keep same course same speed. . . ." He encouraged himself by thinking there was a confident ring about it. Still, it was damned easy to be confident away at H.Q. He only wished he could share the same confidence. The more he considered it, the less hopeful he became. He stared out across the illimitable miles of desert surrounding him, the vast sandy sea upon which his squadron was a mere speck. He felt appalled. Someone, he thought, is searching for us in this trackless eternity All they've got to guide them is a bearing and a speed figure. It no longer seemed to him a matter of course that the twain should meet. Instead, it struck him that it would be in the nature of a miracle if they didn't miss. He foreshadowed all sorts of little things that could go wrong. And seized with a sudden misgiving he snatched his compass and took his bearing again.

One-One-O. Right on the dot. . . . Just as he had wirelessed Kata. Thank heaven, he hadn't made any error there. . . . Still, that didn't alter the unpleasant fact that the desert was a hell of a big place in which to find anybody in a hurry.

He turned round to take another look at his pursuers. They were coming on remorselessly at their ten miles an hour. " And all the fuel to burn they want," he reflected savagely. The 2-pounders, firing fairly steadily, were kicking up the dust with their solid armour-piercing shells at irregular intervals all along the intervening strip of desert. Oppressed by his own anxiety he imagined he could detect signs of increased confidence in the enemy, as though they knew their prey could not escape them now.

He glanced at his wrist-watch. Only fifteen minutes more petrol. Once again with his glasses he swept the horizon from left to right as far as he could see. Then back again. And back once more.

" So that's the verdict . . ." he murmured, lowering his glasses reluctantly.

He disappeared within the tank and clamped down the turret. There remained only one thing more to do. Raising the microphone to his lips, he wirelessed the squadron :

" Continue moving as long as you can," he said. " It looks certain we've got to make a fight of it. . . . Do your best. . . . Good luck. . . ."

He shouted down to his driver : " It's a fight, after all."

The driver nodded without turning his head, and the Squadron Commander ran an eye over the Vickers to make sure that everything was ready for the finale. After which, he turned the cupola and concentrated his attention on the red flashes that sprang every now and then from the long, low dust cloud rolling up after him.

He took another glance at his watch. " In five minutes," he said to himself, " I'll break the news to Kata. . . . I'll bet the only reply is : ' Keep same course same speed.' "

The idea brought a faint ironic smile to his lips.

" Well, the chances are I shan't be here to receive it, anyway. . . . Blast this business. . . ."

Suddenly his earphones sprang to life. It was the commander of 3-Troop speaking from his tank on the extreme right of the line.

" Big dust away on my right, sir. Coming towards us," said the voice.

The Squadron Commander couldn't swing his cupola round fast enough. But he saw nothing distinctly through the dust that swirled round the tanks on his right. Opening the turret he thrust out his head. The dust along the line still obscured the field of vision.

" Speed up a bit. . . . Steady . . ." he yelled to his driver, and the sudden spurt took him out in front of the squadron clear of the dust.

He glued the binoculars to his eyes. Yes, by God, he could see it now. . . . Heaven-sent dust ! . . . A long wave of it, sweeping over the desert towards them on their right flank, at twenty miles an hour.

Soon the wave was near enough for him to discern through the fog the outlines of the squat monsters it enveloped. Cruiser tanks. . . . One . . . two . . . three . . . four. . . .

He counted nine. A whole squadron. And by now he could distinguish the long slender muzzles of their 2-pounders jutting out from underneath the turrets. And the sight was good to one who, perforce, had been confined to thinking in terms of Vickers for nearly thirty very bad minutes.

Behind him, without warning, sounded a terrific crack of gun-fire. He swung round to see what the devil had been let loose. A happy smile broke over his face. The Italians, too, had realised the full significance of that new dust-cloud. The light tanks could wait. Their battle-line had pivoted to face the urgent danger, and was now thundering forward on a long ragged diagonal to meet the cruiser squadron. The crack that had almost startled the Squadron Commander was their parting salute to him.

" I hope they realise they've said ' farewell ' and not just ' au revoir,' " he commented grimly.

It was no longer his show, and he wasn't sorry. As the Italian tanks swept off on their new course, he signalled the squadron to halt. " Break off now for some light refreshment," he added, feeling that it was not entirely undeserved.

The light refreshment consisted of a grandstand view of the tank battle. Crew commanders emerged, head and shoulders out of turrets, and drivers popped their heads through their hatches. They had nothing to complain about on the score of excitement. Less than a couple of miles away, the two long lines of tanks were racing to meet one another, shrouded in two long yellowish billows of dust that rolled onward like rival surfs in a frantic hurry to break on the same stretch of sand. When only a thousand yards separated them, the Italians opened intense fire, the red flashes darting out continually along their front like fiery little serpents that refused to be smothered under the thick pall. Their solid 2-pounder shells kicked up the dust in scores of thick plumes all around the cruiser tanks.

The space between the two long waves narrowed. So far, the British squadron's guns had remained silent.

" By God . . . they're leaving it late," muttered the Squadron Commander, as the distance rapidly decreased, and still the cruisers withheld their fire. But he noticed with satisfaction that the Italian shooting was becoming erratic, many of their shells now falling well behind the British line.

"Ah! . . . They've got that one . . ." he exclaimed suddenly.

The billow of dust had rolled on leaving behind one of the cruiser tanks, motionless on the desert. For a few seconds the Squadron Commander watched in apprehension, half-expecting flames. Then he saw the turret open. A man clambered out and crouched down low, inspecting the side of the tank.

"Track trouble," the Squadron Commander said with relief.

Not more than four hundred yards now separated the two approaching dust waves. And at this moment the British 2-pounders opened fire. A tremendous explosion, like the sharp crack of thunder overhead, reverberated through the desert, accompanied by a sheet of orange-coloured flame that swept right along their front. The Squadron Commander had time to see a couple of Italian tanks stop dead. Black smoke began to pour out of them, followed in a few seconds by little tongues of fire. He saw a tiny figure leap from one of the turrets. Then the two dust clouds seemed to meet and mingle. Everything became confused and obscure. The smoke from the guns on both sides as they continued to fire with the utmost rapidity, combined with the swirling dust to blot all details from view. All the Squadron Commander could distinguish, apart from gun flashes, were the turrets of the two Italian tanks which had been knocked out in the beginning, and which now began to glow like red-hot cinders.

After ten minutes the firing died down. The smoke drifted away and the dust cloud settled. The Squadron Commander lowered his glasses with a grunt of satisfaction. Four of the Italian tanks were on fire. Five others were stationary with cruiser tanks in close attendance. The captured crews were being slowly shepherded over the desert towards where his own squadron had halted, by the Cruiser Commander himself. Far away, scurrying towards the hazy horizon, were the only two of the enemy tanks that had managed to make good their escape.

The Cruiser Commander drew up alongside, his hot, red face beaming with pleasure.

" What did the show look like from the gallery ? " he asked with a laugh.

" First-rate," replied the Squadron Commander enthusiastically.

" Yes, I think it wasn't a bad effort," replied the other modestly. " You put the job in my way, though. Nicely calculated bit of work, yours. I feel terribly indebted to you," he added, with sincerity.

" The debt's all mine," replied the Squadron Commander grimly. " If you hadn't shown up when you did, we were finished. The damn fools didn't fill up this morning. There's hardly a cupful of petrol left between the lot of us. I don't mind confessing that for the last quarter of an hour I've been sweating blood."

" Why on earth ? " inquired the Cruiser Commander, lifting an eyebrow in surprise. " You knew we were coming ? "

" I knew something was afoot. But whether you'd find me was another matter."

" Couldn't avoid doing so," said the Cruiser Commander, amused. " Didn't we have your bearing and speed ? What more do you want ? My boy, it strikes me you've wasted a ' flap.' "

" ' Flap,' be damned ! " retorted the Squadron Commander. " How big do you think the desert is when you look at it ? Anyhow, I consider it was a bit of luck you found us at all."

" Nothing wrong with the desert, old chap," laughed the other. " Wide open spaces where you can see for God know's how many miles. . . . Dust clouds to help you locate things from above and below. . . . In fact, damned hard *not* to be discovered, sometimes."

The Squadron Commander, growing quite hot on the subject, opened his mouth to demolish this statement in the light of his recent personal experience. But suddenly he shut it again without a word.

" Funny," he reflected. " That's myself speaking. That's exactly what I myself have been thinking for months. And now it sounds all bloody rot. Something's happened to me . . . I don't know what it is . . . But it's something good."

Remembering the discomforts of his old obsession, and wondering if the Cruiser Commander would develop on the same lines, he contented himself with saying :

" You know, I could easily become sorry for you."

V—CASE ADJOURNED, SINE DIE.

" You will proceed to Cyrene, and be responsible for the internal security within the area stretching from Derna to Luigi da Savoia, and south as far as Battisti. Your duties are to maintain order between the Italian civilian population and the Arabs. To facilitate this you will contact at once the Bishop of Cyrene, who is French-speaking."

Such, in effect, were the orders the Don R. had just brought along to R.H.Q. from General Staff, Cyrenaica Command. The Colonel read the instructions over a second time, and liked the look of them less than ever.

" Bit of an innovation, this, isn't it ? " he said dubiously to the Adjutant. " Sort of thing that usually falls to the infantry. They're used to it. But it's a new job for gunners."

" We'll take it as an honour," laughed the Adjutant. " Let's see what the map says."

He drew his forefinger roughtly round the area bounded by Derna—Luigi da Savoia—Battisti.

" That's the lot, sir," he said.

The Colonel looked staggered. " It can't be an inch less than two thousand square miles," he exclaimed.

"A bit more, I should think," the Adjutant replied, cheerfully. "They've certainly bestowed on you, sir, what may be termed wide powers of jurisdiction."

"Thank God the country isn't very thickly populated," said the C.O. "You know, I can't say I feel very keen on this policeman business," he added, uncomfortably. "It never seems to me to be a soldier's job. Well, I suppose we had better begin by contacting this bishop."

The Adjutant's mind ran on severely practical lines.

"I suggest, sir," he interposed, "that first of all we equip ourselves with an H.Q. that will be in correspondence with our new dignities. The best available building in Cyrene seems to be indicated. It will help to impress both the Arabs and the Eye-ties with the importance of the new Department for Internal Security. The more they can see the better they'll understand."

"What do you suggest?"

"The Albergo Cyrene, sir," replied the Adjutant, without hesitation. "It's the *de luxe* hotel. Graziani's staff used it as their headquarters. I think we can assume from that, it will suit us. Hot-and-cold in all the bedrooms."

"Water?"

"Basins only, at the moment. But we can soon get the water supply working."

"Sounds an excellent idea," said the C.O.

"Yes . . . There's a lot to be said for this internal security," laughed the Adjutant.

It was nearly a month after Beda Fomm, the brilliant battle in which the Armoured Division cut off the retreat of the remnants of Mussolini's legions from Benghazi into Tripoli, and brought the Italian domination of Cyrenaica to a crashing downfall. Throughout the province, large sections of the Arab population were taking advantage of the disappearance of their masters to pay off old scores upon the Italian colonists who had been planted on their soil, and who now looked to their erstwhile enemies, the British, for protection.

The Colonel, whose regiment of 25-pounders had been encamped in the neighbourhood of Cyrene for several days, had seen quite enough to convince him that anyone taking on the job of establishing internal security, as the phrase went, would have no cause to complain about lack of material. The district seethed with racial jealousies and hatreds ; for the most part openly avowed by the Arabs, and by the Italians cherished with a fervour none the less bitter because it was discreetly subterranean. The Colonel hadn't any powerful sympathies either way. Worthy as the achievements of the Italian colonists might be, he couldn't overlook the fact that, despite Beda Fomm, they still remained the enemies of his own people. As for the Arabs, he detested the orgy of looting they had engaged in the instant they realised the Italian power was broken. You couldn't journey along any of the desert tracks for long without coming across some Arab or other accompanied by half a dozen donkeys laden with green-painted furniture, the standard Mussolini pattern, plundered from the homes of outlying farmers. These with their families, in dread of losing their lives as well as their green furniture, usually fled for protection to one of the larger colonist villages where the local Italian mayor still endeavoured to exert some authority.

Also, the Colonel could not forget the Museum at Cyrene. He had strong archæological leanings himself. The sight of the floor of the museum, covered a foot deep with the shattered fragments of priceless sculpture and pottery which had been excavated from the sites of the ancient Greek and Roman cities in the neighbourhood, was not calculated to endear the Arab to him. When the Adjutant ventured to point out that it was a tenet of the Moslem faith to hold the graven image in abhorrence, the Colonel retorted : " That might carry for the busts. But what about those exquisite vases ? "

Needless to say, he did not include the entire Arab population in his strictures. There were many decent folk among them, he knew. But the mob of looters kept his enthusiasm for the liberated people on ice. He was, in fact, in an excellent frame of mind to deal impartially with both Arab and Italian.

Within a day or two, R.H.Q. (now also H.Q. for the local department of Internal Security) was installed in the Albergo Cyrene, charmingly situated on top of the escarpment, with a view of the blue Mediterranean over towards Apollonia, thirteen miles away. After their long sojourn in R.H.Q.'s consisting mainly of the office truck and a canvas awning under the desert sky, the marble-pillared vestibule of Marshal Graziani's ex-residence, with its black and white chequered floor, and wide marble staircase sweeping up to the first floor came as a pleasant change. The Ordnance Mechanical Engineer got busy with repairs to the water-pump half-way down the hillside, and soon the hot-and-cold was running in the bedrooms and the bathrooms just as the Adjutant had predicted. Sappers put the generating plant at Apollonia into working order again, and electric light was added to the luxuries. A sentry with fixed bayonet paced before the entrance day and night. Looking from his balcony down the hillside where the ancient city of Cyrene lay in beautiful ruins, with its Temple and Grotto of Apollo, its solemn trees, and a fresh-water spring bubbling out of the cliff face in a miniature cascade, the Colonel became more than half-reconciled to his new responsibilities.

The " Bishop of Cyrene who was French-speaking " proved to be a myth. When they tried to contact him they found there was no such person. They discovered a Bishop of Derna. He was non-French-speaking. So that didn't carry them far, they having no Italian or Arabic of their own. But they managed to equip themselves with a Maltese interpreter. His Arabic had been picked up in Palestine, and did not seem to have borne too happily the transplantation to a thousand miles westward. Still, it was good enough to make a start with, and the Colonel had a penchant for wasting no time in getting down to a job.

As it was obvious that, of the two parties, the Arabs were in the most aggressive mood, the Colonel began by summoning all the mudirs—the local sheikhs in his area—to the Albergo for some straight talking. In order to impress them with the importance of the occasion a couple of sentries with fixed bayonets ushered them into the room which had formerly been the hotel-manager's office, where the Colonel sat with the Adjutant and the interpreter at one side of a desk, while six empty chairs awaited the visitors on the other. On the wall behind hung a big map of the area with the various districts of the mudirs plainly indicated in different colours. The mudirs were a queer collection. Four of them looked like excellent under-studies for Shylock. They wore Arab head-dress and dirty, flowing garments that had once been white. Three were entirely tooth-less; the other had the advantage of a couple of long, yellow fangs in which his lips occasionally got caught. The Colonel passed these over as normal specimens. But he took an instant dislike to the chief mudir, a youngish man about thirty, who resembled the sleek, varnished villain of a Hollywood film, complete with smartly-cut European jacket and riding-breeches, highly-polished brown boots, swarthy face, hooked nose, and oily black hair brushed well back. He smelt considerably of perfume, wore a lot of gold rings on his fingers and talked volubly in Arabic that was not always the Arabic of the interpreter. A very venerable old fellow with a long white beard and a benign expression, the Biblical patriarch type, completed the odd assortment. The Colonel thought he had never seen a face that conveyed the impression of so much stored wisdom and experience of life. He was nearly forty himself, and had learned many things. But in front of this ancient, sagacious countenance he felt like a child. At once he conceived a great respect for this old Arab, and hoped for more reasons than one it would never come to a tussle between them.

The Colonel wasted no time in coming to the point.

" King George the Sixth of England, Emperor of

India," he addressed the mudirs, " has sent me here to keep order between your followers and the conquered Italians. You must impress on your people that England is determined that hatreds between yourselves and the Italians must cease. From now on Italians are forbidden to enter your camps. From now on you must forbid your people to enter Italian villages or townships without the authority of a permit from me or the Town Major of Derna. Any Italian caught interfering with your people will be severely punished. Any Arab caught on an Italian cultivated area, or grazing camels or goats on arable land used by Italians will be severely punished. Make this known at once to all your people. It is your responsibility."

While he spoke the six mudirs kept their shrewd-looking eyes fixed on his face, watching attentively the slightest change of expression. When he stopped they flashed sharp glances at one another. All of them remained silent with puzzled, resentful faces, except the patriarch whose benignity still apparently remained unruffled. The Colonel quite understood why they looked puzzled. For two years they had been taught that the more hostile they showed themselves to the Italians, the better the English would be pleased. And now the English were telling them they would be heavily punished if they didn't cease their hostility. Such a *volte face* aroused their deepest mistrust. They couldn't understand how enemies ceased to be enemies overnight. The transition was too swift for them. The Colonel felt a bit sympathetic towards them on this account, but with six pairs of watchful eyes trying to penetrate his most secret thoughts, he took care to preserve his stern demeanour.

" I have arranged that your districts shall be regularly visited by armed patrols," he continued. " Each patrol will be accompanied by an Arab appointed by the mudir of the district, and an Italian selected by the mayor of the principal village. In that way, both sides will have fair play. Every morning the patrols will send in to me reports of any case of infringement of my orders that need investigation. The guilty offenders, Arab or Italian, will be severely punished. Is that quite clear? Have you any questions to ask?"

A flood of Arabic suddenly descended on him. The six mudirs burst into torrents of excited speech, accompanied by much gesticulation. To cope with it was quite beyond the powers of the interpreter. He shrugged his shoulders helplessly. The Adjutant, forgetting he was not back in England at a shareholders' meeting, rapped on the table for silence. The Colonel's pet Alsatian from Benghazi who had displayed his distrust of the mudirs ever since their entrance by continually twitching his nose, began to growl. At last the volubility of the perfumed, Europeanised mudir subdued the other five.

" All the good land has been taken by the Italians for agriculture," he was understood to be complaining, angrily. "We want it back to graze our flocks on."

" You've been here for nearly two thousand years and never cultivated anything," said the Colonel, incautiously.

Whereupon terrific arguments and expostulations ensued. Injuries and grievances were dragged from the distant past, questions of landmarks and expropriations were raised, appeals for immediate restitution were made. It all led nowhere, and the Colonel's patience became exhausted. He rose from his chair to indicate that the audience was at an end.

" I am not in a position to deal with those matters," he said, " I am here to preserve order in the district and I intend to do so, with, I trust, your co-operation. If you have any hesitation about that, take a look at the proclamation outside the Albergo before you leave Cyrene."

The proclamation was one announcing the death penalty in cases of looting and burning.

*   *   *

Early in the afternoon about a fortnight later, a security patrol consisting of a subaltern, a sergeant, two gunners armed with rifles, and the customary pair of Arab and Italian " eye witnesses," was proceeding in a couple of regimental trucks along the undulating tarmac road through the scrub country from El Gubba to Luigi da Savoia. Since the Colonel's interview with the mudirs his patrols had been indefatigable in policing the extensive area under his jurisdiction. He was not dissatisfied with the results so far. There had been no serious disorders. Both the mudirs and the Italian mayors appeared to have accepted his authority in the proper spirit. He knew that donkey-loads of green-painted furniture still passed surreptitiously along the desert tracks, but looting on the grand scale had definitely declined. He received every morning at nine o'clock reports from the patrols on the cases that required investigation. Though in the main these were not serious they involved much time and labour in the straightening-out. Petty accusations were supported and controverted by hosts of equally unreliable witnesses on both sides. The Colonel spent hours trawling in seas of lies and prevarications for a few true facts on which to base his judgments. It was irksome, especially as the weather grew hotter, and the smell of Arab mellowed. But he was far too conscientious to spare himself. Only one thing tried his patience. This was what the Adjutant had christened the " tit-for-tat game." A complaint lodged by an Arab against an Italian was invariably followed by an Italian complaint against an Arab. And vice versa. Each side seemed determined not to let the other score any advantage in the matter of quantity. It was the quality of these accusations that exasperated the Colonel. They were so obviously trumped-up for the occasion.

The above-mentioned patrol had just passed the spot where the grey broken-down arches of the ruined Greek aqueduct, each stone of which still bears the mason's mark, stretch for a hundred yards to the right of the road. Suddenly two Arabs on horseback appeared in

the distance, riding towards them, shouting and waving
to attract attention. The subaltern halted the patrol,
and waited till they came up. Something had evidently
excited the men very much. A torrent of Arabic flowed
from them, emphasised by violent gestures of the hands.
They continued speaking without a pause for half a
minute, and the subaltern was no wiser. He guessed it
was a matter of importance from the grave look on the
face of the Arab in the truck. But the latter was unable
to speak English. Finally, one of the Arabs on horseback managed to pronounce two words that the subaltern
could understand. The words were : " Man killed."
He pointed back in the direction from which they had
ridden. The subaltern nodded and ordered the patrol
to follow the horsemen.

After bumping five miles through the scrub they drew
up at a little Arab encampment, half a dozen low tents
made of brown matting with naked children playing
outside, hens pecking about and dogs barking. A repul-
sively dirty woman squatted in front of a pot suspended
over a small fire. There followed more shouting and
gesticulation, and an elderly, crafty-looking Arab, evidently the headman of the clan, emerged from one of
the huts and, according to the usual laws of hospitality,
invited the subaltern to have a cup of tea. The officer
politely refused and indicated that he wished to see the
body of the dead man. The headman disappeared into
one of the huts, drove out a couple of women and
beckoned the subaltern to enter. He did so, almost
having to crawl on his hands and knees through the
low entrance. Inside the stench nearly stunned him.
When he recovered he saw the body of an Arab dressed
in shabby black garments lying on a mat in the centre
of the tent. The man was dead enough. He had been
shot in the back.

Gasping for fresh air the subaltern fled from the tent
before he was completely overcome. Outside, he produced his message pad and wrote to R.H.Q.

" Body of shot Arab in encampment at ——." (he

gave the six-figure map reference). " Please send interpreter back by truck."

"Jump in your truck and take this to the Adjutant,"
he said to the sergeant. " Get back as quickly as you
can."

Next morning the Colonel sat in his office at the
Albergo Cyrene listening to the subaltern's report.

"From what I can gather, sir, three brothers set off
on horseback from the Arab encampment the day before
yesterday for Derna, with the object of buying some
camels and goats. One of them, so the Arabs say, carried
on him the sum of 1,700 lire. All were unarmed. Just
before reaching the main road, three men on horseback
came into view and without provocation opened fire
at them. The Arabs galloped off. The men fired again.
One of the Arabs fell from his horse. The others continued their flight for some time, till they discovered
they were not being pursued. Two hours later they
plucked up courage to go back. They found their companion lying dead. He happened to be the one carrying
the money. That was gone."

"Did they recognise the three horsemen ? "

"One of them, sir. The Arabs say they can identify
him. He was wearing a white cap with a big peak,
and rode a piebald horse. They say his name is Giovanni
Papini, an Italian colonist who lives at the house numbered twenty-three on top of the hill on the main road,
five miles from Cyrene."

"That seems to simplify matters," said the Colonel.
"Are they sure it was this man ? "

"Positive. I got the pair of them to take me to the
spot where their brother was shot, and asked them to
point out the direction from where the firing had come.
I made a close search of the ground with a couple of
gunners, and we found these."

He placed on the desk two empty cartridge cases.

"Italian pattern, all right," said the Colonel, turning
them over. " What about the bullet in the man ? Same
type ? "

The subaltern hesitated. " I'm afraid I don't know, sir," he said apologetically. " The body was in such a dreadful state I insisted on its being buried at once. I had a lot of trouble with the headman."

" Why ? "

" He didn't want it buried."

" Overcome with grief ? "

" Not at all, sir. He wanted to keep it as evidence. I had to tell him very firmly that it wouldn't keep."

" Well, the piebald horse and the white cap will do to get on with," said the Colonel. " Arrest this fellow Papini and get his statement. Search the house for arms."

So began a troublesome fortnight during which the Colonel learned that the course of true justice, like that of other good things, does not always run smooth. The accused man was duly arrested and lodged under guard at Battery H.Q. in a farm outside Cyrene. There he was examined by the Battery Commander. The Colonel was informed in due course that the man vehemently protested his complete innocence and ignorance of the crime. His wife, and the neighbour in the twin house built beside his, were prepared to swear that on the day and hour of the murder he had been at home. On the other hand, he did possess a white cap with a large peak, and a piebald horse. His house had been thoroughly searched for arms, but none had been found there or at the house next door.

Without being a Solomon, the Colonel possessed a very nice sense of justice, and liked to see its scales working as delicately responsive as those of a laboratory balance. This is excellent in theory. In practice it entails considerable labours and revisions of opinion on the part of the holder of the scales, when the slightest breath of new fact or even personal suspicion immediately shifts the balance one way or the other. So it was with the Colonel. And, apart from his own natural desire not to make any mistake in a matter of life or death, there was his knowledge that his decision was of considerable

importance to the future order of the district. So he
did not spare himself to ferret out the truth.

At first it had seemed a simple case. The white cap
and the piebald horse spoke for themselves. The accused
man's strong alibi certainly complicated things. His two
witnesses were probably quite as worthy of belief as the
two Arabs. Even if that wasn't saying much. Still,
there remained the white cap and the piebald horse. . . .

In the beginning the Colonel had been inclined to
accept this as damning evidence. But, considering the
affair in odd moments during the day, he began to feel
there was something queer about it. He wasn't quite
sure why this feeling grew. It was vague and instinctive.
As far as he could put into a thought the new drift of his
mind it was that the " thing appeared too pat."

A visit next morning from the Italian mayor of the
district to which the accused man belonged, yielded him
further weight to put in the scale against the white cap
and the piebald horse. The mayor opened with a new
series of complaints against Arabs for grazing their flocks on
land tilled by the colonists. The Colonel listened patiently.
He guessed the real reason for the visit, and waited.

" It is a difficult time for my unfortunate people,"
said the mayor. " I trust to you, Signor Commandant,
to see that they get justice and are protected against the
false accusations of their enemies."

" They shall be," said the Colonel.

" Even Giovanni Papini, who is accused by them of
murder ? " interposed the mayor eagerly.

The Colonel nodded. " If the accusation is found to
be false."

" Giovanni Papini is a very good man. A very good
man," said the mayor earnestly. " It is impossible for
him to commit murder. I have known him many years.
He is thrifty and industrious. There is no peasant in
the district who keeps his farm in better condition. I
assure you, Signor Commandant, he is a very good man."

" You will be able to give evidence as to his character
when his case comes up for hearing," said the Colonel.

" You intend to send him to Barce for trial ? " inquired the mayor, in distress.

" I did not say so."

" These Arabs are wicked men. Not like Giovanni," continued the mayor. " They were bad brothers. They quarrelled and fought among themselves always. Their word is dirt."

" Thank you for your visit," said the Colonel, rising from his chair, and the mayor departed.

" I'll bet you, sir, we can expect a call from the mudir," said the Adjutant. " As soon as he hears the mayor's been here, he'll waste no time."

" Make a note to have a few inquiries made about the relations existing between those three brothers," said the Colonel.

The visit from the mudir predicted by the Adjutant occurred early next day. It was the glossy, perfumed mudir whom the Colonel had disapproved of at first sight. As it happened, he was the big shot of the district where the murder had taken place. The victim was one of his tribesmen.

The mudir's approach to the object of his visit proved even more circuitous and wearisome to the Colonel than had been the mayor's. He fenced around the subject for nearly an hour, hoping to draw the Colonel, who gained a mild satisfaction out of disappointing his efforts. Finally he launched into a tirade against Italian colonists who hired Arab labour at half the wages they had formerly been in the habit of paying. It was, he alleged, one of the principal sources of unrest in the district. There were some notorious cases. The Arabs looked to their English friends to protect them from oppression by these grasping tillers of stolen soil. They were bad men. All of them as bad as the murderer whom the wisdom of the *miralai* (colonel) had caused to be arrested.

" What murderer ? " asked the Colonel, blandly.

" The Italian assassin, Papini," replied the mudir, lifting his eyebrows in surprise. " Surely there is no doubt ? "

" There is, till the man has been tried and found

guilty," said the Colonel. "That is English law, which I am here to administer."

The mudir was silent for a moment. Then, with his dark, smouldering eyes fixed steadily on the Colonel's face, he said softly:

"I and my people have great respect for the English law. It would be much sorrow to me if anything happened to make us lose it."

The veiled threat in the remark was not lost on the Colonel.

"Damn the fellow's impertinence," he thought, meeting his searching glance with an impassive face.

"This man Papini," he observed. "Did he underpay his Arab labour?"

"He was the worst. My people all spit at him," replied the mudir.

"Thank you. And now I am very busy," said the Colonel, terminating the interview.

"Ask them down at battery H.Q. to find out whether this man Papini was in the habit of underpaying his Arab labourers," he said to the Adjutant when the door closed behind the mudir. "It's an interesting point, though that fellow wouldn't have been so ready with the information if he'd known why I asked."

"Damn cheek of him to try that bull-dozing business, sir," commented the Adjutant.

"Yes. But it does indicate that this affair is causing a bit of a ferment in the district. That's one reason why I don't want to make any mistake."

"You know you've got the case down for hearing to-morrow, sir?"

"Postpone it for a couple of days. I want to do a bit more thinking about it," said the Colonel.

When the two days had passed the Colonel was still undecided. The Battery Commander reported that it was quite true the accused man had a very bad name among the Arabs for cutting down wages. Also, it was quite true, as the mayor had said, that the dead man and his two brothers were usually on bad terms with

one another.   Thirdly, the accused man's alibi had been
considerably weakened by the discovery that his next-
door neighbour had been away from home for part of
the day on which the crime took place.   The Battery
Commander sent along reports of the statements of
dozens of witnesses, Arab and Italian, some more relevant
than others, but all equally conflicting.   These the
Colonel waded through with much labour, and digested
with much thought.   But they brought him no nearer
to any definite conclusion.   Curiously enough, it was
still the most damning piece of evidence against Papini—
the white cap and the piebald horse—that convinced him
the least.   The more he thought about it, the stronger
grew his instinct that there was something fishy there.
He pored over the documents with a thoughtful brow.

"This case is getting on your mind, sir," ventured the
Adjutant.

"I believe it is," agreed the Colonel, a bit wearily.
"I suppose I ought to have committed the fellow for
trial to be arranged by G.H.Q. at Barce, long ago.   But
I don't like sending him up till I'm certain in my own
mind that he's guilty.   I'd feel I was shelving responsibility."

"That white cap and the piebald horse ought to justify
you, sir."

"They would have.   If I hadn't damned well started
thinking too much about them.   The trouble with me is
I want to be sure.   And I'm not.   After all, murder's a
serious matter, and this man's life is at stake."

"The Arabs seem determined to have his blood."

"Yes, and if they don't they won't like it."

"You don't think he's innocent, sir, surely?"

"I wish I did.   Or didn't.   Either way, it would be
a load off my mind.   It looked a pretty simple affair to
handle, to begin with.   But it doesn't seem so cut-and-
dried now.   The only thing I feel sure of is that I'm
groping for the truth in a welter of lies, on both sides.
Here's a point that strikes me as curious.   From the
statements of the two Arab brothers the motive of the

murder sticks out as robbery. Yet in all that mass of evidence there isn't a word to indicate that Papini knew the three were carrying a large sum of money on them that day, or even that he knew they were going to Derna at all. Then it seems to me an interesting coincidence that out of the three brothers, the one who got shot happened to be the one who is said to have been carrying the money. A lucky shot for Papini and his associates in the circumstances. And though the two brothers are very positive about Papini, they have the haziest descriptions to give of the other assailants. In fact, they don't seem much concerned about them at all."

" You don't suggest, sir, it's a frame-up ? "

" No. I haven't gone quite as far as that," said the Colonel. " But if it were a question of a frame-up, there's no one more likely to be selected than Papini. You've heard how unpopular he is with the Arabs ? "

" Still, sir, you can't get away from that piebald horse and white cap."

" No, I can't. In more ways than one," replied the Colonel, thoughtfully. " I think I'll have a talk with those two brothers myself," he added. " Have them brought along here to-morrow morning at ten."

" And I'll let Battery H.Q. know that the hearing of the case is postponed again. Till when shall I say, sir ? "

" Better leave it open," said the Colonel.

The interview with the brothers of the murdered man lasted for some time. It had been an afterthought on the part of the Colonel, and he did not expect much from it, beyond allowing his instincts concerning the white cap and the piebald horse to have free play during the conversation. He said little himself, and was content to listen patiently while the Arabs related volubly and at much length the details with which he was already familiar from their earlier statements. Watching their sharp-beaked faces and glittering eyes, they reminded him of a couple of vultures with their talons already fixed on their prey. Still, he was forced to admit to himself that they told a pretty convincing tale. One new fact he elicited which interested him. Both the brothers had at periods in the past worked on Papini's fields, and both complained that he had paid them badly.

" You know this man Papini well ? " he asked.

" Yes, Excellency."

" You knew he wore a white peaked cap and rode a piebald horse ? "

The Colonel spoke as though he were extremely sceptical of their knowledge.

" Why, yes, Excellency. Otherwise how should we have known that it was him," they hurried to assure him.

" All right. That will do," said the Colonel, dismissing them.

" Not very fruitful, sir," remarked the Adjutant. " We're where we were."

" I'm afraid so. And yet there's something about that piebald horse and white cap that I can't quite swallow. You heard how eager they were to point out that it was by these they recognised Papini. And how anxious they were to insist on their knowledge that he possessed a piebald horse, etc. I know it points to a straight bit of identification. At the same time, if their object was to pin a crime on him out of spite, the fact that they already knew he wore a white cap and rode a piebald horse would simplify their job very much."

" We'll get no further, sir, without the help of a detective out of a novel," said the Adjutant.

Very reluctantly the Colonel had to admit that he would be compelled to hear the case, and come to some decision with his mind still unconvinced either way. It was a fortnight since the murder had taken place. He couldn't justify any further delay. It aggravated and depressed him slightly to feel that he was beaten. He had devoted much time and thought to the affair, and that scrupulous sense of justice of his remained dissatisfied with the result. It gnawed at him like an uneasy conscience. Just that one grain or two of certainty that would have contented him was missing. He thoroughly disliked the idea of sending the case to Barce for trial without having first come to a definite conclusion about it himself. But there was no more he could do. " Thank heaven, the power of life and death in the affair does not rest with me," was his one comforting reflection.

" I'll hear the case on Wednesday," he informed the Adjutant. " Have the accused and all the witnesses here by ten o'clock."

Entering the office at nine on the appointed morning, the Adjutant found the C.O. already at his desk, deep in a last perusal of all the statements of the witnesses.

" I'm happy to think, sir," he said, " this fellow Papini will not be our concern much longer."

The Colonel looked up with a frown.

" I'd feel happier myself if I could have made up my mind about him," he said wearily. " I'm sick of wading through these statements. Lie *versus* lie, most of it. I suppose I shall have to send him to Barce to take his chance. . . . Perhaps I want to be too positive. I weigh up things too carefully. But, after all, this fellow's life is at stake. On the face of it he is a bowled-out murderer. And yet . . ."

He broke off as the door opened and a Don R. entered with a message, which the Adjutant took and read.

" Look at this, sir," he exclaimed, passing it to the Colonel. " Something's happening."

The message was from G.H.Q., Barce, informing the Colonel that the regiment was to move up towards Benghazi immediately.

" This means only one thing," said the Colonel.

" War broken out again . . ."

" Yes. Germans this time. I knew we'd been expecting an attack, but not quite so soon. There's real fighting coming now."

" Means good-bye to the good old Albergo. And to Internal Security," observed the Adjutant.

" And I'm not sorry," said the Colonel, with feeling.

The telephone rang. The Adjutant picked it up. It was the Battery Commander to say that he was just leaving for the Albergo with the accused man, Giovanni Papini, and a couple of lorry loads of witnesses.

" Stop him, for God's sake," shouted the Colonel, hurriedly. " We've got other things to think about now."

He grabbed the telephone.

" Dismiss those witnesses," he instructed the Battery Commander. " The case is adjourned. Sine die."

The Battery Commander did not catch the last phrase, so the C.O. repeated it.

" Sine die. . . . Which I hope means for ever, so far as I am concerned. I've just had a signal from G.H.Q., Barce. We've got to be on the move early to-morrow morning. Come along here immediately for orders."

The Battery Commander wanted to know what he was to do with the prisoner.

" Oh, damn the prisoner ! " exclaimed the Colonel, as if this was no time for trifles. " Forget him. In any case, he isn't our pigeon any longer, thank God. Pass him over to the Town Major at Derna, if you feel like it. Let him have a crack at it. A nice headache will do him good."

He relinquished the telephone and commenced to hum a cheerful tune. A load of uncomfortable responsibility seemed to have dropped from his shoulders as if by magic. Giovanni Papini's troubles faded from his mind like something that had never been. A pleasant comfort stole upon his conscience. The prospect of soon being in action again exhilarated him. He plunged with the Adjutant into the arrangements for the regiment's departure. He hadn't felt so pleased with himself for days.

VI—FORLORN HOPE

THE Machine-Gun Corporal was writing home to the girl he hoped to marry.

It was a sunny afternoon at the end of March. The

corporal sat on the edge of the bed—an Italian one—in the big, whitewashed barrack-room with a stone floor, just at the foot of the water-tower at Benghazi, where his company was billeted. The midday meal had come and gone. Three or four men of his section lay stretched out on their beds digesting it, with the comfortable aid, of such sleep as the horde of stinging, swarming flies that filled the room with their buzzing, permitted. Though the day was hot, they had drawn the blankets completely over their heads, and lay still and featureless like shrouded corpses in a mortuary. The corporal had an open window just above his head, through which, now and then, entered little puffs of warm and somewhat gritty air. Every few moments he paused to brush away the dust that kept settling on his sheet of notepaper. High in the sky outside, a couple of British planes, off on a reconnaissance, droned steadily. But the drone of the flies within the barrack-room sounded more insistent.

The corporal, a dark-haired, dark-eyed, lean-faced young fellow of about twenty-six, with a sallowish complexion, continued to write :

" You'll know by now from the papers all about how we mopped up the Eye-ties. We've made a proper job of it, I give you my word. As far as I can see the war's over in this part of the world for a good while to come. Carnera's taken the count. . . .

" We've been here getting on for nearly two months. Looking after prisoners most of the while. Thousands of 'em. . . .

" All the boys are expecting, now the job's finished, we shall be packing up for Cairo as soon as the reliefs come up. And I hope they won't be long coming. The Aussies have already gone back, and it ought to be our turn next. . . .

" And if anyone's due for leave it ought to be me, after more than six years' service abroad. If the war hadn't come along I'd have been home long ago, and we'd have been put together by the parson, and been old hands at the game now. . . .

"But I don't reckon we'll have to wait much longer now. I'm pretty sure to be one of the first on the leave-boat when we return to Egypt. And all the chaps say that may happen any day now. There's nothing more doing here. . . .

"Only the other day our captain was saying that when we get back to Cairo we'll be able to draw our big pay. I've got a nice bit coming. And what with that and the other bit I've put by during the last five years, you won't be making such a bad start. And I wouldn't be surprised if I get a step up. And then you'll draw sergeant's separation allowance. Not that you care so much about that, I know. No more do I. The chief thing is, you'll be mine and I'll be yours, for keeps. . . ."

The corporal had proceeded thus far when a heavy footstep echoing along the stone floor checked the flow of his optimism. The Company Commander had just walked in, and seemed to be in a hurry. The corporal jumped to his feet, still holding the unfinished letter in his hand.

"Find the sergeant, and tell him to call all the men together . . . here," said the captain briefly. "I've got some good news for them."

"Good news . . ." As the corporal hastened away in search of the sergeant the two words buzzed in his head like the flies in the barrack-room. It could only mean one thing . . . Orders to pack up for Cairo. He was glad now that he hadn't mailed his letter the day before. He'd be able to tell her something definite now. He'd sit down when the Captain had gone and begin his letter all over again. And really let himself go. . . . It was rather peculiar, though, the expression on the Captain's face. Something set about it. Not the kind of face you'd expect to go with good news. At least, not such good news as going back to Cairo. . . . Still, what else could it be ? . . . Hadn't the Captain himself said it ? . . . "I've got some good news for them. . . ."

In a few minutes all the Company not engaged on duties were sitting on the beds in the barrack-room, grouped round the Company Commander. A tall, sinewy man, he towered above them as he stood in the centre of the floor, slapping his thigh with a cane as he waited for the scraping of feet and the murmur of conversation to die down.

" Quiet, everybody ! . . ." shouted a sergeant.

Silence fell on the barrack-room, broken only by the buzzing of the flies. Every eye was fixed on the officer. Like the Corporal, each man anticipated an announcement that they were packing up for Cairo. And, like the Corporal, most of them were thinking that the Captain had a funny way of looking ' good news.'

" I've called you here," began the Company Commander, in a steady, matter-of-fact tone, " to inform you that the Colonel has chosen this company to proceed forward to Mersa Brega to meet the Boche."

The buzzing of the flies in the barrack-room could be heard louder than ever.

" That's some hundred and fifty miles west of Benghazi, on the coast road," continued the Captain. " Half a brigade will be up there to meet the attack, and we shall be supporting them. What I particularly want to impress upon each one of you is this. You'll be fighting a very different enemy from the Italians. Boys could have beaten them. At Mersa Brega you'll be up against a tough, determined, cunning foe. It won't be any picnic. Every man must do his best. Take no chances. If you halt anywhere on the way up everything must be camouflaged and concealed, as in all probability you'll be dive-bombed and machine-gunned."

The Captain paused and surveyed the assembled faces.

" Any questions ? " he asked.

No one spoke. No one moved. Then the Corporal, with thoughts of his unposted letter, said :

" How long are we likely to be there, sir ? "

" God knows," replied the Captain. " It may be three days, or it may be three months."

Again there was silence, while the men chewed the cud of their disappointment. It wasn't that they were impressed by the idea of fighting Germans. They were quite confident they could deal with Jerry as easily as they had with the Italians. But they had been so confident they were due for Cairo. This new development knocked all their expectations on the head. They had been positive that the fighting was over for a long while to come.

The Captain understood what was running through their heads.

" We've been picked for the job, and we've got to make the best of it," he said abruptly. " I'll tell the sergeant-major to see that you take all the best vehicles. That's all."

The men sprang to their feet and he strode from the barrack-room. Slowly the Corporal tore his letter up into tiny fragments, and, when the room emptied, dropped them out of the window.

Next day, having overhauled the guns and got up extra ammunition, the machine-gun company departed from Benghazi. The Company Commander had gone forward earlier with a reconnaissance party, leaving the Second-in-Command to bring the company along to Mersa Brega. He rode in front in his little " pick-up." Behind followed the eighteen or so trucks containing the three platoons, two 15-cwt. vehicles carrying C.H.Q. gear and a Bren gun on a Motley mounting, and a couple of 30-cwt. lorries with the stores, rations, cooking kit and so on. They wound down the dusty coastal road in a long, very attenuated line, keeping a distance of four hundred yards between each vehicle in case of a sudden air attack. Nothing happened, however. There wasn't a single enemy plane to be seen in the blue sky. Eventually, when nearing their destination, they met the Company Commander waiting for them in the road. He escorted them to the chosen area, which was some two hundred yards in front of the village, among the sand dunes close to the sea, at the top of the Gulf of Sidra, facing the Tripoli border. In the brilliant sunshine, the glaring white of their new surroundings dazzled them. Stretches of white, slightly undulating sand in front and to each side of them, and behind the white houses, and the white minaret of Mersa Brega sticking up conspicuously against the blue sky. Utter silence pervaded the place. The village had been entirely evacuated. Not a soul was to be seen. The only sign of the enemy was a lot of rusty barbed wire which the Italians had long previously erected some thirty yards in front of the village.

Amid this scene of bleached isolation the machine-gunners settled down with the rest of the meagre British force to meet the first onslaught of Rommel's Afrika Korps. Though they didn't know it at the time, it was a very forlorn hope. They dug themselves in with feverish haste, knowing full well that there wasn't a moment to lose. They built up the gun positions with sandbags, and strengthened them further in front by constructing a ramp out of layers of stones covered with sand, twelve feet thick, to prevent bullets coming through. The Vickers guns were mounted on sandbag tables raised in the centre of the gun-pits. The Corporal's section was on the extreme right of the defensive line, and his own gun-pit occupied the end position fifteen yards from its fellow. Looking to his right he could catch a glimpse of the sun sparkling on the deep blue waters of the Mediterranean. Just behind him ran the trench in which the section commander, a sergeant, had his control post.

The night passed quietly. Next day was April 1st, and as the morning wore on without sign of enemy activity the Corporal turned to his loader as they leaned over the parapet of the gun-pit and, in the spirit appropriate to the day of the month, expressed a wonder whether " Jerry was making them one." The loader let it be very definitively known that he wouldn't grumble if Jerry was. It was almost immediately made plain to them that Jerry wasn't.

A thick flock of Stukas emerged from the western horizon early in the afternoon. In a few minutes they were over the British positions. Then the machine-gunners underwent a dive-bombing experience such as had never been theirs before. The Stukas, one after the other, dropped down screaming from a height of over ten thousand feet, as if they were going to crash right into the gun-pits. When scarcely a hundred feet above the ground they unloosed their bombs, broke their descent, and began to climb upwards again at a perilous angle. Under the shock of the continuous and terrific explosions, the gunners crouched in the slit trenches half dazed and deafened. A couple of Bofors guns, somewhere in the rear, barked away, but made little impression on the Stukas. The machine-gunners had their Vickers laid on fixed lines, so as to cover the whole zone of desert in front of them in case of an infantry attack. They did what they could to cope with the dive-bombers with their Bren gun and rifles. The mere effort of retaliation provided some satisfaction, though it made no difference to the Stukas. From behind the invisible German lines yonder among the sand dunes in the west, more arrow-shaped formations followed to take the place of the Stukas that had unloaded all their bombs and emptied their machine-gun belts.

For two hours the attack continued without cessation. All along the forward positions the earth was continually flung up into the air in huge fountains. From farther off echoed dully the explosions of the bombs that were being dropped on the troop positions and lines of communication behind. At the gun-pits the machine-gunners felt themselves completely cut off from the world. Clouds of white dust enshrouded them, through which the sentries peered painfully with red, smarting eyes to detect the first sign of an enemy infantry advance. By now the village had completely disappeared, its pretty white houses flattened into heaps of rubble under the bombs. The Corporal, looking out of the trench for a moment, was just in time to see the minaret get a direct hit, and collapse like a pack of cards. And as though the destruction of the minaret had been their great objective, the Stukas seemed to decide to pack up now this had been achieved. They flew back to the German lines, with puffs from the Bofors shells dotting the sky behind them. An uncanny silence settled upon the earth with the settling dust. The long drawn-out ordeal was over.

The Corporal and his gun crew crept back to their pit. They had been lucky. Not a man had received so much as a scratch, and although a couple of bombs had burst close in front of their position, no harm had been done. Their truck in the rear had also escaped, for which they uttered hearty thanks. It meant that in a short while they were regaling themselves with a meal of bread and cheese, and jam, and tea, prepared by the driver whose job it was to act as chef. After the events of the past two hours they felt they deserved it, if only to wash the dust out of their throats.

The Corporal, who rather fancied himself as a letter-writer, was thinking he would have something to write about in his next, when the quiet was broken by a sinister whine overhead, and a shell burst in the air with a peculiarly vicious crack.

"Shrapnel! . . ." he shouted, and once more they crouched as the bullets hummed around their ears.

In a few moments they were enduring a second inferno, more nerve-shattering even than the first. The Germans had started to shell the positions with shrapnel. Fortunately their range was slightly on the long side. Most of the shells burst over the wrecked village in their rear. But as is the nature of shrapnel, the stuff spread in all directions, and the men could hear it singing through the air and slapping ominously against their sand-bags.

"Keep your eyes peeled," the section commander in the control post bawled to the sentries. "Looks as if they intend putting in an attack soon."

For the next half-hour the shrapnel continued to rain round them. The bombardment all along the line developed in intensity. The air was never free from the devastating crack of the shells. In the middle of it all one of the sentries shouted that he could see movement in their arc of fire.

In the control post the section commander stared intently through his binoculars.

" Enemy advancing . . ." he roared above the din.

Oblivious of the shrapnel, the gun crew sprang into action, the Corporal standing up behind his gun on its table. On his right the loader gave a last glance to see the belt was in order. The section commander seized a range-finder to get a more comprehensive look at the zone in front of him.

He could now distinctly see the little figures of the German infantry clad in a lightish khaki uniform, advancing over the sand dunes in sections of sixes and twelves. Although the machine-gunners' arc was a good one—120 degrees—the whole place seemed alive with the little figures. The section commander, unperturbed, noted the range. It was 2,000 yards.

" Wait till they get to sixteen hundred," he shouted to the Number Ones in the gun-pits. " It's only infantry. We can hold them all right."

One of the ammunition numbers added another couple of wooden boxes, each containing 500 rounds of ammunition, to the three already in the gun-pit. More were stacked in a trench close by. The Corporal stared steadily forward over his gun across the desert. A few minutes passed without a word, while the shrapnel continued to whine and crack overhead.

" Here they come," he said at last to the loader. " Loads of 'em. By the look of it they must think we've all been blown to bits. They're going to get a surprise."

The enemy infantry were, in fact, advancing over the dunes methodically, in fairly close order, and without taking much trouble to look for cover. It gave the Corporal satisfaction to think of the welcome prepared for them. One man in particular he made a note of, a gigantic officer, some way in advance of the rest, and conspicuous among the peak-capped soldiers by his steel helmet.

Behind, the section commander took another squint through the Barr & Stroud.

"All . . . sixteen hundred . . ." he bellowed. "Black patch . . . left . . . ten o'clock . . . three degrees . . . right and left two taps . . . lay. . . ."

In the gun-pit the Corporal bent forward slightly and looked along the sight of his gun. He elevated it and then depressed it a little, taking as the centre of his aim the tall officer in the steel helmet. Along to the left of him the other machine-guns of the company were already in action, and a few shells from the scanty British artillery were dropping among the distant sand dunes. But the Corporal continued his preparations with cool, unhurried deliberation.

"On . . ." he announced in a moment or two to the loader as he straightened himself up and looked steadily over the top of the gun towards the advancing enemy, his two thumbs on the thumb-piece.

The loader, his eye on the section commander, stretched his arm out horizontally behind his back to signal that they were ready. Immediately the section commander raised the flat palm of his hand and dropped it. The loader tapped the Corporal smartly on the back.

Still gazing fixedly in front of him, the Corporal pressed the thumb-piece, and the sharp rattle of the fire echoed in the gun-pit. The Corporal fired in bursts of twenty-five, stopping for a brief moment every now and then as he tapped the traversing handles, right and left, so as to sweep completely his arc of fire.

The sudden withering fire from the machine-guns seemed to give the enemy the surprise the Corporal had anticipated. All along the front the advancing sections appeared to thin down considerably, and numbers of little figures lay motionless on the ground. The rest hurried to seek cover among the dunes.

"That's a bit for them to go on with," observed the Corporal as he pressed the thumb-piece again. "Next time they won't be so careless. Hope I've got that big bloke in the tin hat. I've taken a dislike to him."

"I hate the bloody lot," grunted the loader. "They've done us out of our trip to Cairo."

" I was just writing to my girl to tell her I hoped to be home soon," said the Corporal, sending off another burst.

" What a hope ! " exclaimed the loader. " Seems to me this war's begun all over again. Wonder how Jerry likes having to do the Eye-ties' job for him. Not much, I should think."

" I tore my letter up," continued the Corporal, pressing viciously on the thumb-piece.

" Safest place for it," said the loader briefly.

The shrapnel continued to crack over their heads, and now the Germans were putting down a heavy H.E. barrage a few hundred yards behind the forward positions. Once more the machine-gunners had the feeling that they were cut off from the rest of the world. This didn't worry them, however. They had every confidence that they would soon smash up the infantry attack.

The advance had indeed been slowed down appreciably. For a while the arc of fire seemed to be emptied of the little figures, except for those that lay still on the ground.

" Looks like we've halted them," said the Corporal.

" They'll come on again," prophesied the loader. " They aren't Eye-ties."

The loader proved correct. A few minutes later the ground was swarming again with the enemy infantrymen, steadily creeping forward and making short dashes from one dune to another. The rain of bullets that swept towards them seemed to make no difference to their methodical progress.

" Stop ! . . . " yelled the section commander, seeing the range dropping. " All down one hundred. . . . Go on. . . . "

Once again the Corporal pressed on the thumb-piece, firing in rapid bursts and flicking the gun to right and left in order to spray thoroughly his arc. Looking over the top of the gun, his eyes fixed on the little darting figures in front of him that continued to press forward despite the terrific fire, he began to think that things were going to be tougher than they had expected. He reluctantly admitted a sort of professional respect for these new adversaries. The loader passed the tag of a new belt through the feed-lock.

" You're right," said the Corporal, brushing his sweating forehead in the pause. " They aren't Eye-ties."

The range continued to drop. Twelve hundred . . . Ten hundred . . . Nine hundred. . . . Although the ground was covered with dead and wounded, the enemy still pressed on. They seemed to become more numerous than ever, dotting the dunes as far as the eye could see. There was no lack of targets for the gunners. They took the nearest as being the more dangerous. The only trouble was that the more they knocked over, the more appeared.

Eight hundred and fifty yards. . . .

" Gun control . . ." shouted the section commander, leaving each gun free now to act for itself. His job in the control post was over, and he came forward to lend a hand in the gun-pit on the left of the Corporal's.

" Getting a bit hot, ain't it ? " observed the loader cheerfully, fixing a new belt. " Where the hell are they all coming from ? Looks to me like the whole bloody German army. How many of us did the Captain say there was up here ? "

" Half a brigade," said the Corporal with a grin.

" Well, that ought to be enough," replied the loader ironically. " Ammo . . ." he shouted over his shoulder, as if to emphasise his opinion that in the circumstances they could not have too much.

A couple of the ammunition numbers darted forward and dumped two more boxes of belts by his side.

" There he is," suddenly exclaimed the Corporal.

" Who ? "

" That long bloke in the tin hat that's leading them," he explained. " I thought I'd got him."

He tapped the gun slightly to the left in the direction of the German officer and pressed the thumb-piece in a short burst.

" Bull's-eye ? " asked the loader.

" Don't know," answered the Corporal. " He's disappeared for the time being. I could see that bloke encouraging the others. Waving 'em on. Wouldn't do any harm to knock him over."

Seven hundred yards. . . . Six hundred yards. . . . Five hundred yards.

Steadily the range decreased, despite the ceaseless and deadly machine-gun fire. Behind the gunners the H.E. barrage continued with unabated fury, pulverising what the Stukas had left of the village. It was now getting on for seven o'clock, and twilight was beginning to fall. Suddenly the Corporal, taking a swift look over the distant dunes, blew his breath against his teeth with a hissing noise.

" What's up ? " asked the loader.

" Panzers . . ." said the Corporal laconically.

" Panzers ? " echoed the loader sharply.

He peered over the parapet of the gun-pit and saw what the Corporal had seen. Six sandy-coloured heavy tanks, slowly moving along a track on the right of the arc, about a thousand yards distant. They were travelling in extended order, with a wide gap between the first two and the remaining four. Crawling along over the dunes in the gathering dusk, they looked like some strange amphibian monsters, newly emerged from the bottom of the sea upon a vast primeval beach. The loader gazed at them for a moment or two in silence.

" That does make a difference," he said solemnly to the Corporal.

The Corporal didn't hear. He was busy putting in another burst of fire. But it did not need the loader to tell him, or any of the men in the gun-pit, that their circumstances had undergone a decided change for the worse. Hitherto, they had not been much bothered by the infantry attack, persistent though it had been. All the time, they had remained confident that sooner or later it would wither away before their fire. They had implicit faith in their weapons. But panzers were a very different cup of tea. They knew that against them their Vickers wouldn't be much more effectual than a boy's catapult. It altered in an instant their whole view of their immediate future. They knew definitely that now they were in a tight spot, unless some relief came quickly. And, knowing how thin were the numbers and how meagre the equipment of the little British force that was bearing the brunt of the Afrika Korps' first onslaught upon Libya, their hopes were not lofty. They prepared themselves to see it out to the grim end.

The Corporal dispatched a man to the section commander to report the appearance of the tanks. The man returned with the information that the sergeant had seen them himself, and had already sent a runner to the platoon commander of the infantry on their left.

" Not that it'll be much use to us," commented the Corporal. " They'll probably be in the same boat as we are. I hope they've got a lot of 25-pounders back in the rear."

It was now dark enough to see the flashes of the panzers' 2-pounders as they began to fire at the forward positions. After a little while they vanished out of sight down a shallow wadi on the right. As the minutes passed without their reappearance, the men in the gun-pit began to cherish vague hopes that they might have gone for good.

In the meantime they had other matters to occupy their attention. As if encouraged by the arrival of the panzers, the enemy infantry put in a most determined attack, though the machine-gunners raked them with belt after belt. The Corporal saw the lot that concerned him most rush forward across a depression without faltering. In front of them ran the tall German officer. To the Corporal he loomed up in the half-light as a personification of the enemy's tenacity, and a personal challenge to his own powers. He took a swift glance down the sights, tapped the gun slightly to the right, and pressed the thumb-piece. The tall officer continued to run on. Not so his men. The concentrated fire had at last proved too much for them. All along the front they sank to cover behind a wavy ridge of dunes only three hundred yards from the British forward positions.

The tall officer continued to run forward, practically

alone. He half-turned to wave his men on with the revolver in his hand. The Corporal gave him another burst. He stumbled and fell, struggled to his feet again, and staggered on. Again the Corporal pressed the thumb-piece. The tall officer fell, rose again, took a few paces blindly forward, and dropped. This time he rose no more. His dead body lay within a hundred and fifty yards of the gun-pit.

" That bloke took a lot of killing," said the Corporal with satisfaction. He was elated at his success. In some dim way the downfall of this man, whom he had picked out as highly dangerous when the advance first began, seemed symbolical of the eventual defeat of the attack. His spirits lightened for the first time since the arrival of the panzers. Once more he felt fully confident of victory.

The gunners were now firing to keep the enemy infantry down. From their positions in the dunes, only three hundred yards away, success rockets soared into the sky to announce to headquarters behind that they had reached their objective.

A man crawled into the back of the gun-pit with a message.

" Other gun wants to know if we can let 'em have any ammo," the loader informed the Corporal. " They've run out."

" Let 'em send back for some more," said the Corporal shortly, dispatching another long burst at the top of the dune ridge in front.

The trucks with the reserve ammunition were some three hundred yards behind them to the left, beyond the old Italian wire.

" They sent a couple of men some time ago," replied the loader. " They haven't returned. Must have been cut off in the barrage. There don't seem any chance of getting through. We're not too well off, ourselves," the loader added gravely.

" How much ? "

" Four boxes."

"Let 'em have half," said the Corporal, without looking round. "We must keep that bunch in front pinned down. Send a couple of men back to the trucks. They've got to get through somehow. We're in a jam."

Two of the ammunition numbers crawled out of the back of the gun-pit and departed on their perilous errand. The minutes sped by without their return. The Corporal continued to fire at the slightest indication of movement by the enemy. They themselves were now subjecting the gun-pit to rapid fire from rifles and automatics, but most of the bullets embedded themselves in the thick stone-and-sand ramp in front of the gun-pit. A quarter of an hour passed with no sign of the men who had been sent to the trucks.

The loader tagged another belt to the gun.

"Make a hit every time, Corporal," he said solemnly. "That's the lot."

Twenty minutes had now elapsed since the panzers passed out of sight. In the interval, the Corporal, beset by the immediate dangers of the situation, had almost allowed them to pass out of his mind. It was rapidly getting dark now, and he wondered whether they would be getting the order for withdrawal at nightfall. If not, they'd have to take their chance. He wouldn't mind that so much, if only that blasted ammunition would arrive.

Suddenly, just as he was about to release another short burst at a suspicious movement to his front, there was a loud swish in the air, followed by a terrific explosion just outside the gun-pit. The Corporal and the loader were flung bodily to the back of the pit, where they lay for a few moments while a shower of falling stones and sand descended on them.

"God Almighty ! . . ." exclaimed the loader, as soon as he could get his breath. "What was that ? . . . A bomb ? . . ."

The Corporal staggered to his feet and stared over the broken parapet of the gun-pit.

"Panzer . . ." he shouted hoarsely.

The panzer had come up behind the dunes on the

right unseen, and was slowly moving towards them.
Another shell burst near the gun-pit next to them.
Desperately the Corporal traversed the gun in the direction
of the new peril. He heard groans coming from behind
him. The remaining ammunition number had had his
right eye knocked out by a shell fragment, and was
leaning up against the back of the pit, holding a handkerchief to the bleeding socket.

"Tell him to make for it," the Corporal told the loader.
And the half-blinded man clambered out of the rear of
the pit and disappeared.

The Corporal straightened himself up, rigid as a statue.
He stared towards the tank over the top of his gun
and pressed hard on the thumb-piece in a long burst.
He knew it was futile. But he intended they should
have all he'd got to give.

"Only half a belt left!" yelled the loader.

The panzer was now so close that they could see the
white-outlined swastika painted on the side of the turret.
It moved towards them, inhuman, relentless. Thirty
yards away from them it stopped. Its turret was now
level with the gun-pit which had been constructed on
the forward slope of a low dune.

Again the Corporal fired. The response was immediate.
A tongue of red flame leaped from just below the turret
of the panzer, and the shell burst right inside the pit.

The loader came to his senses amid a welter of choking
smoke and sand. The gun had been blown off its mounting and the Corporal was lying near it on his side, groaning.

"You hit, Corporal?" asked the loader anxiously.

The Corporal struggled to sit up, and succeeded in
raising himself on an arm.

"They've put me down for keeps," he said with
difficulty. "You get off. I'll do what there is to be done."

The loader expressed his reluctance to leave the
Corporal alone.

"You clear out, I tell you," insisted the wounded man.
"You can't do anything for me. It's all over. I won't
be seeing Cairo . . . or anything else. . . ."

" I'll take the lock," said the loader.

" You get out," said the Corporal forcibly, with an effort. " I'll look after the lock."

The loader gripped him by the hand.

" Good-bye . . ." he said hoarsely.

Left alone, the Corporal, who was mortally wounded, dragged himself to the gun. Laboriously, and breathing hard, he lifted up the rear cover and removed the lock. He set himself to the task of stripping it, piece by piece.

The Vickers' lock consists of eighteen separate parts.

VII—WHEN THE PENDULUM SWUNG BACK

THE short, eager-faced young Battery Captain, who belonged to the 25-pounder battery away down at Mekili, had been out on a reconnaissance for the most part of the afternoon. He had appeared on the escarpment five miles to the east of Barce early that morning to make preparations for his battery, which was expected to arrive from Mekili in a day or two to join in the attempt to stem the rush of Rommel's Afrika Korps, which was now sweeping forward from Benghazi. A couple of British infantry brigades, mainly Australians, and one regiment of artillery stood in their way on the sides and top of the steep, stony, treeless escarpment. Some of the gunner regiment's 4·5 howitzers were sighted on the green plain that stretched before Barce. Others, a little farther back, covered the approaches from the south. It was believed that the enemy were feeling their way eastward along the desert tracks as well as by the coastal road, in the hope of cutting off the British Division. At any moment their armoured patrols might show up. In the circumstances, the addition of a battery of 25-pounders to the defences of the escarpment seemed, to the gunner regiment now in sole possession, a happy thought. The Second-in-Command took the new-comer under his wing, and conducted him over the gun area, and gave him the benefit of the experience they had gathered during their own two days' occupation of the ridge.

It was after five o'clock before they returned to the scrub-dotted cleft in the valley where the three or four vehicles that constituted R.H.Q. were tucked away. In front of the office truck the Adjutant sat at a trestle-table occupied with some writing. He glanced up as they approached.

" Picked some nice Troop positions ? " he inquired.

" There are possibilities," laughed the Battery Captain.

The Adjutant shook his head. " No, there aren't," he replied. " None at all."

They stared at him in surprise.

" See these," he continued, tapping the forms he had been preparing. " Time-table and route sheets for the big flit. All ready for the C.O. when he returns."

" Where is he ? " asked the Second-in-Command.

" Hob-nobbing with the Brigadier. He got a call to go over to H.Q. at four o'clock. I'm expecting him back any moment."

" P'raps it's only another flap," said the Second-in-Command. Two nights previously they had suddenly received orders for withdrawal, but after travelling about five miles it was discovered to be a false alarm, and they all had to turn round and come back. A very unpleasant business in the pitch darkness, and one which the Second-in-Command was not anxious to be repeated.

The Adjutant shook his head.

" No flap this time," he said confidently. " The C.O.'s got a hunch. And you know what his hunches are like."

At this moment the C.O.'s truck deposited him at their side, and one look at his face showed them that another of his hunches had come off.

" We move at 20.00 hours (8 p.m.)," he announced, and gave the Adjutant the map reference of the track and road junction that would be their starting point.

" Fill in the times and order for the units to move on to the road. R.H.Q. moves first. The Division is going right back by stages to Tobruk. Route will be Tecnis-Maraua-El Gubba, by road. Then turn off right, and by desert track to Martuba. Then back on the main road through Bomba. Derna's become dangerous, so we're side-stepping it. Report centres will be established at El Gubba and Bomba. There'll be a petrol dump some six miles west of El Gubba at the road junction. Inform all concerned."

" What about you ? " the Second-in-Command asked the Battery Captain when the C.O. had departed. He understood the unpleasant feelings of a man separated from his own battery at such a juncture.

" I must get back to Mekili and rejoin my battery."

" If it's still there," added the other doubtfully. " You heard what the C.O. said. There may be German tanks in the place by now."

" Well, I've got to get back to it," said the Battery Captain stubbornly.

" Best thing for you to do," said the Second-in-Command, after a moment or two's thought, " is to come along with us till we cut across the Derna-Mekili road. Then, if you want to, you can turn off to Mekili. If your battery is withdrawing, as is very likely, you may run into them coming up the road."

The Battery Captain turned the position over in his mind for a bit.

" Yes," he nodded. " I don't see anything else for it."

Already preparations for the withdrawal were in progress all along the escarpment. There wasn't a minute to be lost. No one could fail to recognise the urgency of the moment, now that it was certain the Germans had pushed forward with tanks across the desert to the south of them. It was a race to prevent themselves from being cut off in the rear. And even now it might be too late. On top of the escarpment smoke was rising in the windless air from scores of fires where the Australians were burning supplies and equip-

94

ment they were unable to take along with them. On the ridge the howitzer batteries hurried forward with their own packing up. It was past six o'clock and they were due to move off by eight. So the Troop Commanders and the Wagon-Lines Officer put in some heavy overtime while the ammunition was loaded into trailers at top speed, vehicles refuelled, and rations stowed away in the mess lorries. Meanwhile the cooks busied themselves preparing a last good meal for the men, it being extremely doubtful when they would get their next. The " quads " —the four-wheel-drive towing vehicles—were brought up close to the guns in readiness. But the guns themselves remained on their lines till the last moment. There was always a possibility that the head of the German columns advancing along the coastal road might suddenly appear from the direction of Barce. For the same reason the telephone wires were left intact.

However, the last anxious half-hour passed without sign of the enemy.

Ten minutes before zero hour the guns were limbered-up, the telephone wires cut and jettisoned, and they moved off to their starting point, with the Troop Commanders bringing up the rear of their Troops. It was now just getting dark, and a three-quarter moon was rising in the cloudless sky. At first they had a fairly clear road. The timing arrangements had worked well, and the regiment fitted neatly into the vast column of transport that spread over the road for mile after mile—nearly a thousand vehicles of all types : lorries laden with infantry, Bren-gun carriers, all the paraphernalia of Division H.Q., guns, ammunition trailers, " quads," R.A.S.C. lorries, Signals trucks—all crawling along in the faint light of the moon on the first stages of this new Retreat of the Ten Thousand that was not to end till they came to Tobruk, nearly two hundred miles away.

For several miles progress was steady and orderly, and the vehicles kept their distances fairly well considering all head or tail lights were forbidden. But as the light improved with the rising of the moon the whole column underwent a transformation. It was as if the sight of the ghostly, scrub-covered country surrounding them infected everybody with a sense of its ominous mystery, and filled every mind with the same urgent need for hurry. Everybody speeded-up. Everybody wanted to overtake the person in front. Very soon the road was jammed with a confused mass of vehicles, three abreast. Distances were no longer kept. It was nose-to-tail now. Lorries crashed into one another, and crashed again when they tried to back, wheels interlocked, trucks were squeezed off the road and had difficulty in getting back again, guns became mixed up with infantry lorries and had no hope of regaining touch with the rest of their batteries, men cursed and swore in the darkness at unseen obstructors, and at frequent intervals long sections of the column were held up while some particularly bad mess ahead was being disentangled. To make matters worse, there suddenly appeared from nowhere a regiment of Royal Horse Artillery, and some vehicles of an armoured division. They claimed their share of the road and added to its prevailing chaos.

The Second-in-Command, alone in his truck with a driver, hadn't the faintest notion where he was in respect to the rest of the regiment. He had started off with the R.H.Q. unit when they left the escarpment, but much had happened since then. He fully expected that the guns were by now dispersed over miles of the road, and having the same bad time as the rest of them. And he was right. He hoped that he still had one of his Signals trucks right behind him. He had ordered it to keep in touch with him as he had no wireless in his own truck, and he wanted to feel ready for any eventualities. He was in a pessimistic frame of mind, and it would never have surprised him to see half a dozen German tanks suddenly loom up out of the uncanny, moonlit desert. He was even more pessimistic about his truck which exhibited every intention of sooner or later breaking down. Every time he went into top gear it would spit and spit till it was changed down. Driving in such a hell of a traffic jam under these conditions got on his nerves. He and his driver took it in spells, an hour apiece, and each was damned thankful when the change-over came. At last, packed in the middle of a bunch of infantry lorries, the truck came to a dead stop and defied all efforts to make it budge. Shouts, yells and curses were showered on them from the darkness. The Second-in-Command and the driver got out, risked being crushed to death by the vehicles squeezing past them, and with the light of a torch tried to discover what was wrong. After a bit, another truck bumped into them, but the Second-in-Command stopped swearing when he discovered, to his relief, that it was his own Signals truck. The signallers jumped out and helped him to tinker with the vehicle till it showed signs of life again. Then he moved on, with the engine spitting and spitting all the time as before. But a little later the same thing happened again. Another storm of abuse from the darkness, another descent into the perils of the crushing maelstrom, another fifteen minutes' search for sand in the parts by the light of the torch, another coughing, spluttering start. And so it went on. The Second-in-Command began to consider whether he hadn't better abandon the truck altogether and get a lift.

By now it was nearly two in the morning. The column had covered about eighty miles. Everyone was feeling tired and worn out with the strain of driving under nightmare conditions. Men began to fall asleep at the wheel, and vehicles piled up in a confused heap behind them till they were unceremoniously kicked into wakefulness again. The urgent need for hurry that seemed to have taken possession of everyone showed no sign of abating. There was always the grey, ghostly, menacing desert at hand to whip it up. No one could be sure whether the enemy were close at hand or not. Already they might have got across the Mekili-Derna road, and their armoured patrols might be searching the desert for the retreating column. And an attack on the latter in its present condition would mean disaster.

Nearing El Gubba, a new anxiety took hold of them. Would they find the petrol dump at the road junction a few miles farther on, or would the Germans have discovered it first. If so, their chances of getting anywhere near Tobruk were pretty thin. Under this new pressure the desire to push on at the greatest possible speed received added impetus. And the chaos increased accordingly. But the petrol dump was there all right. A few miles farther on their eyes were gladdened by the sight of the big four-gallon square tins, stacked in the scrub by the roadside, and shining in the fading light of the moon.

They punched holes in the tops of the tins, fuelled up, and commenced the second stage of the retreat. Now, in order to avoid Derna and its possible dangers, they branched off the main road into the desert, climbing a steep hill on top of which gleamed the white castellated walls of a deserted fort. The scrub disappeared, the boulders with their blotchy shadows grew fewer and fewer, till at last they had nothing on either side of them but unqualified sand. The moon went down, clouds had overspread the sky, and pitch darkness enveloped everything. In the total blackness, on this desert road that was little more than a track, the column found it impossible to get along at all without occasionally switching on headlights. Hold-ups became more frequent and lasted longer, vehicles wandered off the track into the desert and did not realise it till they found themselves completely isolated, hundreds of yards from the main body.

On the track itself the chaos had assumed a different quality. It was no longer one vast, nose-to-tail jam. It had broken up into thick clots, with empty stretches in between. To the Second-in-Command, continually fearing the final breakdown of his truck, this new mode of progress seemed more nerve-wracking than ever. He would turn a bend in the track, or what he thought was the track, and find himself absolutely alone, unable to distinguish any other vehicle in front or behind. The whole column appeared to have vanished. These sudden transitions from crowded company to utter solitude produced a queer effect. It was as though he could feel the vast empty desert pressing forward to envelop him in all its sinister mystery. It made him imagine he must have wandered off the route. And he pictured himself lost for good in a truck that had given up the ghost. Then he would drive forward desperately and draw a breath of relief when, after a time, he caught up with some fragment of the chaos that previously he had so heartily cursed.

It had turned much colder, and he and his driver wrapped themselves from head to foot in blankets. The keen wind whipped up the sand, driving it through the floorboards of the truck, and adding to the discomforts of the night. As the breeze freshened the sand swirled higher, plastering the wind-screen. So in order to see where they were going they had to keep it lifted, and were soon half-choked by grit and the dust that the other vehicles churned up. The Second-in-Command came to the end of an hour's spell of driving through inky darkness and a miniature dust storm, and thankfully gave place to his companion. Wrapping the blanket tighter round his face to keep off the sand, he settled down to doze. When he awoke the truck was at a standstill.

" Curse it ! Another breakdown ? " he exclaimed savagely.

" Not us this time, sir," said the driver. " Big hold-up in front somewhere."

" How long have we been here ? "

" Full ten minutes, I should say."

The air was noisy with the shouts and curses of all the other drivers who were being held up. And amid the confusion the Second-in-Command heard a voice just in front blasting some " bloody gun." This woke him right up. He got out of the truck, worked his way up the track past about sixteen vehicles, and discovered that the voice was correct. It was a gun that was causing the hold-up. Moreover, it was one of his own howitzers, the first he had set eyes on since the beginning of the retreat. The track narrowed slightly at this spot, with a ditch alongside, and a thick four-foot stone wall, with angular flanking pieces had been erected by the Italians to prevent traffic from tumbling over into the ditch in the dark. One of the quads towing the howitzer had jammed against the end of the wall. It couldn't move forward, and the pressure of the vehicles behind prevented it backing. A harassed sergeant was doing his best to induce them to squeeze back and give him moving space.

The Second-in-Command ordered drag-ropes, with double man-power. The gun was unhooked, the ropes attached, and in the darkness twelve hefty gunners heaved and sweated and grunted, while unseen critics continued to curse them for the delay. The gun refused to budge. One of its wheels had gone too far into the ditch.

" Leave the bloody thing and let's get home," shouted a voice.

" I think I could do it with another half a dozen men, sir," said the sergeant hopefully.

" You shall have them," said the Second-in-Command.

Close at hand was an Australian P.U. truck with driver and spare driver in front. Both were asleep. In the rear of the truck lay four other Aussies, also slumbering hard. All were so weary and worn out that the Second-in-Command had difficulty in arousing them. When he explained that he wanted their immediate assistance at the end of a drag-rope they expressed their feelings in no uncertain language. But they tumbled out, grousing all the time, put their backs into it, and the gun was heaved into the middle of the road.

Fully three hundred vehicles had by now piled up behind them, and seeing that it was one of his own guns that had caused the trouble, the Second-in-Command felt uncomfortably responsible.

" Thank God that's finished," he said to himself as he walked back to his truck after seeing the howitzer hooked in, and the vehicles begin to move forward again.

More trouble awaited him. This time his truck definitely refused to be coaxed into a start. Fortunately the Signals truck had trailed him again in the darkness.

" You'll have to tow me," he said.

While they were fixing a short towing wire, another truck drew alongside and a voice shouted :

" Can you tell me where the hell we are ? "

The Second-in-Command recognised the voice. It was the young, eager-faced Captain who had come up from Mekili to the escarpment at Barce. Since the retreat started he had completely forgotten his existence. Now he remembered.

" You still hoping to rejoin your battery ? " he asked. " I've almost given up hopes of seeing mine again. God knows where they've got to. What a bloody night this has been. My eyeballs feel as if they're sticking six inches out of their sockets from straining to see things. And now this blasted truck has walked-out on me."

" Let me give you a lift for a bit," said the Battery Captain. " I can do with a spot of company."

" So can I," replied the Second-in-Command readily.

He climbed into the front of the truck beside the Battery Captain, whose driver and servant were half asleep in the rear. They started off with the towing vehicle following behind, and the Second-in-Command's first feeling was of relief at something missing. This he discovered to be the spitting and spluttering of the engine that had tortured him for so many hours. " The damn thing must have been getting me down," he thought.

" I suppose you don't know exactly whereabouts we are ? " asked the Battery Captain for the second time.

" Does any of us ? We all hope we're getting somewhere near the spot where we cross the Mekili-Derna road and make for Martuba."

" I'm getting a bit anxious," said the Battery Captain.

" So should I be if I had intentions of looking for a battery in the neighbourhood of Mekili."

" I don't mean that. What I'm afraid of is that I've

already passed the road junction. I've kept my eyes peeled all the time, but it's damned easy to miss the turn in this confounded blackness and confusion. You're inclined to get swept along with the mob. I suppose I shall be the only one that isn't going straight on."

Though the words dropped from the Battery Captain in quite a natural tone, the Second-in-Command received them with a little shock. He had a picture of this tiny fragment of the great chaos, this one truck, suddenly detaching itself from all the rest of the column, and striking off alone southwards into the black mystery of the desert where heaven alone knew what was happening.

" Yes, you will, I expect," he said slowly.

He was conscious of a slight sense of embarrassment as he spoke. He himself was one of those who were going " straight on," leaving the Battery Captain to be swallowed up in the unknown. The contrast made him feel uncomfortable. He knew damn well how he would have hated the positions to be reversed.

" You know, I think it's most unlikely your people are still at Mekili," he said after a puase.

" Possibly not," said the young Battery Captain. " But I've got to find out."

" The Boches may be pretty thick down there by now."

In the darkness the Battery Captain nodded silently. They continued on their way for some time, packed tight in a confusion of lorries that spread right across the track, before he again spoke.

" I'll be dead sure to miss the junction if I don't get out of this jam," he said anxiously. And for some time all his attention was devoted to worming his way towards the side of the track, which was no light task with everybody driving blindly forward, and refusing to concede an inch of space. Eventually he succeeded to the extent of being pushed off the track altogether, and drove about fifty yards into the desert before discovering what had happened.

Once more the Second-in-Command had the sensation of something mysterious and menacing crowding in on him. Exactly as when he had found himself suddenly alone on a stretch of the desert road. He was glad when they got back to the company of chaos, and were crawling forward again by the track. His queer re-pugnance to the idea of the Battery Captain being destined, alone out of the vast column, to drop out and disappear into the unfathomable recesses of the desert, returned stronger than ever. He couldn't adjust himself to the idea. There seemed something uncanny about it. Though it was no affair of his really, he could not rid himself of an uneasy feeling that after the column had passed on he would have a twinge of compunction. As though he had deserted a comrade. As though they had all deserted a comrade. It was ridiculous, he knew. But there it was.

"It wouldn't surprise me," he said at length, "if your battery had pulled out long ago, and were half-way to Gazala by now. That would be their most direct road to Tobruk. Probably, like us, they've been ordered to give Derna a miss. So they won't be coming up the Mekili road and you'll miss them. Very likely they're well ahead of us. In which case, if you stick with the column, you'll be able to pick 'em up later."

The young Battery Captain seemed to be considering the suggestion.

"I think I'll be easier in my mind if I cut down to Mekili," he said finally. "My last orders were to join the battery there. If I can't find them I'll have to come back. That's all."

The Second-in-Command thought the chances about fifty to one that it wouldn't be all. But he held his peace.

Shortly afterwards the truck bumped into something by the edge of the track. They switched on the head-lights.

"Thank God! The junction at last," exclaimed the Battery Captain.

A wooden signpost had stopped them. It pointed in three directions. To Martuba, which was the way the column was going. To Derna on their left. To Mekili on the right, across the desert south-westwards. The column, which had nothing to do but keep straight on, lurched and lumbered past in the same old confusion, hardly noticing the signpost in the darkness.

" Well, we say farewell here," said the Battery Captain cheerfully. " Thanks awfully for the company."

" Without wishing to appear conceited, I trust you won't meet with any worse where you are going," replied the Second-in-Command as he alighted.

He stood by the roadside for a second or two for a final word. The endless column continued to rumble past in the pitch-black night. One tiny fragment of it was about to drop off and disappear, and none out of all the thousands would take the slightest notice, or care a damn one way or the other, since the Battery Captain wasn't anybody's business at a time like this. The Second-in-Command wasn't sentimental. In any case, there hadn't been time enough for the acquaintance with the young Battery Captain to ripen. Of course, he hoped he'd get along all right. But what chiefly moved him was this queer parting of the ways. Such a violent contrast. . . . Something disquietening about it. . . . A bit morbid, even. . . .

The Battery Captain was saying : " To tell the truth, I shall be damn glad to have a road to myself. I'm fed up with swallowing the dust of half a division. My mouth's like a brick kiln."

" I should go ca-canny, if I were you," said the Second-in-Command. " You don't know what has happened down there. Be prepared to turn and run."

The Battery Captain laughed.

" See you in Tobruk," he shouted.

The Second-in-Command watched the darkness and the desert swallow him up. " I suppose I'd do the same myself," he was thinking. " But I'm damn glad it isn't my job."

* * *

It was that darkest hour that precedes the dawn when the Battery Captain broke away from the column and headed south for Mekili, some fifty miles away. The desert lay black and invisible on either side of him, but, unlike the Second-in-Command, he was quite impervious to the haunting mystery of it. It was enough for him that, after hour upon hour of driving in fits and starts, he at last had a clear road with, as he hoped, his own battery at the end of it. He felt very glad now, that he had resisted the temptation to go on with the retreating column. After all, no one knew what had happened down south, and it was just as likely as not that his battery were still in their positions. In any case, he would soon find out. What did bother him was an atrocious thirst. He pulled out his flask of watered whisky and swallowed a mouthful, cursing to find it gritty. Then he passed it to his driver and servant.

" And leave a drop for later on," he admonished them.

They had progressed about twenty miles when dawn came, and the desert through which they were travelling gradually unveiled itself—a drab, indefinable colour in the absence of the sun. As the light strengthened mile after mile was added to their horizons. But wherever they looked they saw nothing but the humped wastes of sand. So far as human activity was concerned, they might have been the last men in the world.

The Battery Captain was just thinking that if the battery were withdrawing he might run into them any moment now, when the driver suddenly exclaimed :

" What's all this in front, sir ? By the side of the road, on the left."

A hundred yards or so farther on a number of articles which they could not as yet define lay scattered about in the sand.

" Looks like a body on the road also," said the Battery Captain, narrowing his eyes.

But it wasn't a body. As they came up to it and slowed down, they saw it was a soldier's black kit-bag. The other articles in the sand also became recognisable.

A soldier's pack, a tin hat, a great coat, a telephone and a reel of wire.

"This ain't Eye-tie stuff, sir," said the driver.

After many months the desert was still covered with the litter from the Italian débâcle earlier in the year. But the Battery Captain didn't need to be told that the equipment he was looking at was British. He jumped from the truck, walked over to the kit-bag, and turned it over with his foot. There, to his amazement, he read the name and number of a gunner in his own battery. He examined the other articles in the sand, but they told him nothing more.

"Well, I'm damned!" he murmured. "What's the meaning of this?"

He took a searching look over the desert and found nothing to enlighten him. Everything was empty and lifeless. So he returned to the truck.

"One of ours," he said tersely. "Drive on a bit. . . . And not so fast."

Another surprise awaited them. Half a mile farther on they came across a burned-out vehicle, twenty yards off the road. It was still smoking. The Battery Captain descended to investigate. Though only the frame of the vehicle remained, he identified it as a British truck. And in his own mind he felt pretty certain it belonged to his own battery. His perplexity grew, and unpleasant forebodings began to take shape in his mind.

Cautiously they proceeded for another quarter of a mile. Their next discovery was an abandoned lorry on the road. It stood mournfully in the middle of a scene of disorder. All around, the ground lay strewn with men's kit-bags. Most of them had been ripped open, apparently in a search for valuables. The discarded contents were scattered in confusion over the sand—socks, boots, shirts, underwear, old letters and post-cards.

Leaving the driver in the truck, the Battery Captain, accompanied by his servant, poked about among this pathetic flotsam and jetsam like a detective looking for clues. But beyond establishing the fact that it *was* his battery, he came no nearer to a solution of the mystery. There were no traces of a fight, no bodies, and, so far as he could discover, no bloodstains on the sand. He turned his attention to the lorry. It appeared to be unharmed except for a bullet through the radiator. The water had run out and made a pool in the road. Once more the Battery Captain asked himself what the devil could have happened. By now he felt certain it was something pretty serious. He seemed to be following a trail of disaster, and dreaded what he might find at the end of it. There seemed something uncanny about the affair. All around, the tremendous unbroken silence and solitude of the desert. And at his feet these mute evidences of . . .

His servant approached. He had picked up one of the post-cards from the sand and was gazing at it with his mouth half open.

"What do you think about this 'ere, sir ? " he exclaimed.

The Battery Captain took a casual glance. He saw the photograph of a girl with a nice smile on her face. At the foot were a couple of rows of inked crosses.

"Yes. Pretty girl," he said abruptly. "But I've got other things to think about just now."

"It's my sister, sir," said the gunner.

"Your what ! "

"Yes, sir. She's Bombardier Wilcox's girl. You know, sir . . . Don-troop. She must have sent it to him. They're engaged to be married."

Looking at the troubled expression on the gunner's face, the Battery Captain understood full well what was passing in his mind. He forced a note of cheerfulness into his voice and replied :

"Well, they have all my best wishes."

"Strikes me they'll need 'em . . . And more," returned the gunner gloomily, thrusting the photograph into his pocket.

Back in the truck, they continued their journey more cautiously than ever. The Battery Captain stood up on a seat all the time, sweeping the desert with his glasses. But he could distinguish no sign of movement anywhere, not even a suspicious dust cloud. For a mile they crawled along, and then, turning a bend in the road where the sand was piled up in a low dune, they pulled up with a jerk. Not far in front of them stood a " quad " with a gun attached. For a moment or two they stared, not knowing what to expect. But no one appeared.

" Wait here and be ready to drive off like hell," said the Battery Captain to the driver.

He drew his revolver, climbed down from the truck, and walked up the road alone. The front of the " quad " pointed towards him, and as he drew nearer he could see the red and blue artillery plate on the bar across the radiator, and the number, painted in white on the plate, that denoted his own regiment. The side doors of the " quad " were wide open.

He crept up as silently as possible, and peeped inside. There was nothing. Only a few cigarette ends and an empty match-box on the floor. Once again he was confronted with a mystery. This time a bigger one than before. The vehicle seemed to be undamaged, and the gun was also intact. It did not appear to have been in action. In any case, it was now hooked in. Again he looked around for bloodstains, but couldn't see any. He climbed on top of the " quad " with his glasses. The road in front was straight and flat, and he could see for miles. He searched the sandy distances attentively for some minutes. He could discover nothing more. The trail of disaster had apparently petered out. He could come to only one conclusion as he stood there gazing on the hooked-in gun. The battery must have been surprised on the road by the enemy. And not many hours before, to judge from the still-smoking truck they had passed. What had happened to the rest of it was beyond his power of divination. He turned and waved to the driver of his truck to come on.

" I think we've rejoined all of the battery that we're likely to," he announced, grimly.

*   *   *

The Second-in-Command was beginning to think life worth living again. He sat in the Signals truck which was still towing his crock behind. But the horrors of the night's chaos were over. The retreating column had shaken the sand of the desert track off its wheels at Martuba, just after daylight. They were now a few miles beyond Bomba. There was confusion and hold-ups still. But you could at least see what was going on. That is, if your eyes weren't too sore and inflamed by the sand to bear the glare of the blazing sun.

Drawing near to a pair of whitewashed houses by the roadside, the Second-in-Command saw his C.O. and the Brigadier standing outside scanning the passing column attentively. He halted and jumped out.

" We are to go into action," said the C.O. " I've already halted two of the guns. They're parked just by that bridge over the dry river-bed. Wait here and collect all the others as they come along. Then take up position near the road facing south. We're to hold the road till all the transport has gone by."

The Brigadier nodded assent and walked off.

" Like that, is it," commented the Second-in-Command.

" We don't exactly know what it's like," said the C.O. " But we've got to be ready for an attack. What we do know is that enemy armoured forces penetrated up the Mekili road to Derna last night."

The Second-in-Command whistled.

" And they missed us . . ."

" Yes. They were a little too previous. Or we were nicely behind-hand," said the C.O. " Anyway, it looks as though they don't know much more about our movements than we do of theirs. So there's a chance we shall get through without any trouble."

He disappeared into one of the whitewashed houses, which had been turned into a temporary Brigade H.Q., leaving the Second-in-Command to gather up the fragments of the regiment. It was a tedious business, keeping an alert eye on the thick, massed, never-ending stream of vehicles that rolled past, snatching a gun out here, and a Troop Commander there. He had almost completed the job when a "quad" came along which, to his surprise was towing, not a howitzer, but a 25-pounder. Even greater was his surprise to discover the driver of the "quad" to be the young Battery Captain whom he had never expected to see again.

"Battery short of drivers?" he laughed, as the vehicle stopped.

"This is the battery . . . as far as I know," replied the Battery Captain, sadly. He gave the other a brief account of his adventures.

"I found the engine of the 'quad' in working order, and there was plenty of petrol," he concluded, "so I thought I'd at least save one gun. God knows what's happened to the others."

"I can give you a rough idea," said the Second-in-Command. "Last night a Boche armoured force came up the Mekili-Derna road. They missed us. We were too late for them. But your people seem to have been on time."

"Blast it!" exclaimed the Battery Captain vehemently.

The bitter look in his eyes stopped the Second-in-Command from congratulating him on his own lucky escape.

VIII—The Sergeant-Major Works It Off

THE Company Sergeant-Major owned a most useful pair of eyebrows. Dark and thick, they arched mildly over his pleasant, frank blue eyes. That was their normal configuration. But when anything occurred to put him out, they flattened into a straight line that brooded over his countenance like a thundercloud. This seldom happened. The Sergeant-Major was far too cheerful and efficient to be readily upset by the usual run of

troubles and aggravations. Three months of harassed
existence on the outer defences of Tobruk had scarcely
altered the contour of his eyebrows once. Still, there
wasn't a man in the company who was unaware of the
implication of the sign whenever it did appear. When
the Sergeant-Major's eyebrows did knit together in that
ominous straight line, no one needed any more telling.
The platoon sergeants understood at a glance that he
was to be approached with caution. And so did the
platoon officers.

It was getting towards the close of a sweltering afternoon in mid-summer. All day long the brazen sun had
beaten down from the cloudless African sky upon the
thirst-tortured defenders of the beleaguered town. The
machine-gun company, in face of continual shelling and
bombing, had for weeks clung tenaciously to their positions just inside the wire to the south-west of Tobruk,
on the left of the Derna road. Half-roasted by the heat
the men lived and fought and died, day after day, in
the burning sand where the gun positions had been dug
and revetted with bits of stray timber, and stones that
scorched like a grill. At night they snatched what sleep
they could in slit trenches leading off the crawl trench
just behind, the Nos. 1 and 2 occupying berths nearest
to the guns in case of emergencies. In front stretched
the parched powdery desert, where the dirty yellowish
sand drifted into heaps around the base of small, low,
grey rocks. Not far in advance were the forward defence
lines of the British infantry. From here the ground
made a gradual slope into a wide shallow dip, rising
beyond to a long sand ridge which denoted the enemy's
position. This was rendered conspicuous in the distance
by the presence of the only outstanding feature in all
these miles of monotonous desert—a squat, cylindrical
erection, grey against the skyline, and resembling a
small gasometer, but known to the machine-gunners
as the Water Tower.

Company H.Q. was a mile or so behind the forward
positions—a cave hewn out of the rock at some previous

date, with a gallery running round open to the air. In the centre stood a trestle table, and nearby an up-turned box for the clerk to work at. On the sandstone walls hung maps of the Tobruk area, marked with the positions of the British and enemy troops, and also their respective minefields. A couple of camp beds were ranged alongside one of the walls. These belonged to the Company Sergeant-Major, and the Quartermaster-Sergeant. The officers came into the cave to work, but lived in a dug-out a short distance away. On another ledge of rock outside the cave dwelt the signallers with their telephone terminal connecting H.Q. to any part of the line and to their own forward positions. As a place of comfort H.Q. had little to offer in advance of the gun positions themselves. It was bare, stark, and business-like, with the possible exception of the broken-down type-writer on the floor, which was so clogged with sand that the mere contemplation of it gave one grit in the eyes.

On this particular afternoon the Company Sergeant-Major was alone in the cave. He sat at the trestle-table with a map of his area upon which he was marking, with coloured chinagraph pencils, the positions of some new mine-fields. These were constantly being altered, and it was one of the C.S.M.'s daily jobs to keep the chart up-to-date, and inform the platoon sergeants in the forward positions what changes had been made. This was a comparatively simple matter so far as their own mines were concerned. But the infantry in the area had a habit of sometimes sowing their mines without advertising the fact. Which was inclined to complicate matters. While the Sergeant-Major concentrated on his task, large desert rats and mice scurried around his feet. He took little notice of them. By now both he and the Quartermaster-Sergeant had grown used to the plague. They were only stirred to drastic action when the rats climbed on to the table and tried to take the food out of their very mouths. Then a broken rifle barrel began to thud.

The Sergeant-Major was marking in the last of the

new mine areas when the Quartermaster-Sergeant entered, having just returned from Battalion H.Q. with rations. He tossed an air mail postcard on the table.

" Bit of mail for you, Sergeant-Major," he said. " The battalion postman had just collected it from Field Post Office. So I brought it along."

The Sergeant-Major dropped his pencil with alacrity. News from home was what he had been hungering after for weeks. He was especially anxious about his wife, whom he knew to be in a very poor state of health.

The Quartermaster departed to give some orders about the rations. When he returned after a few minutes, he was surprised to see the Sergeant-Major still staring at the postcard in his hand. What is more, he noticed that the Sergeant-Major's eyebrows had been drawn down into one thick angry line. He had never seen him look so black and lowering.

" Anything wrong ? " he inquired.

Without speaking, the Sergeant-Major handed him the postcard. The Quartermaster read it over twice.

" Bloody bad luck ! " he said, in sympathy.

He would have liked to say more, but couldn't think of any other suitable words on the spur of the moment. So he repeated himself with added fervour. It was indeed a bad knock for a man, and merited all the sympathy one could express. The postcard informed the Sergeant-Major that his wife's house, his mother's house, and his wife's mother's house had all been bombed in a recent air-raid, and the three women were in hospital. In addition, seven other of his relatives had been killed.

Looking at the silent figure of the Sergeant-Major as he sat at the table struggling to control the ferment of his emotions, with his eyebrows so straight and rigid that it seemed they would never arch again, the Quartermaster felt deeply that here was a case for something more than mere verbal sympathy.

" You'd better have my tin of beer," he said. " N.A.A.F.I.'s just made an issue. You can do with it, after that packet."

In the circumstances human fellowship could go no further. Beer in beleaguered Tobruk was as rare as nectar. The ration averaged out at about half a pint a man in six weeks. The usual practice was for half a dozen to pool their mouthfuls and to toss-up so that at least one man got a decent drink when the ration did arrive. The Quartermaster had won the latest of these gambles and had been looking forward a whole fortnight to the beautiful sensation of beer trickling down the inside of his parched, gritty throat. Hence he felt the extent of the sacrifice he was making. And so did the Sergeant-Major.

" No thanks," said the latter. " Take more than a tin of beer to help me swallow that," he added, nodding towards the postcard on the table.

" You're welcome," insisted the Quartermaster, heroically.

" I know," said the Sergeant-Major, in full appreciation.

They were interrupted by the entrance of the Company Commander. His eye took in at once the significance of those flattened eyebrows.

" Anything wrong, Sergeant-Major ? " he queried, echoing the Quartermaster's words of a few minutes before.

" Bad news from home, sir," replied the Sergeant-Major, enlightening him as to the contents of the postcard.

" I'm very sorry to hear it," said the Company Commander. " I hope the women aren't seriously hurt. Keep your spirits up, Sergeant-Major."

" My trouble's to keep something else down, sir," said the Sergeant-Major, grimly.

He wasn't exactly able to define the nature of this " something." But it was there all right. It included an overpowering urge for immediate action to avenge the injuries inflicted on his kith and kin. But there was more in it than a simple craving for vengeance. Hitherto he had fought hard against the enemy, doing his duty as a good soldier and a good Englishman. Now he felt a fierce desire to strike a blow for himself alone. And he wanted to do so without any delay. He knew he wouldn't be on good terms with himself again till he had. The odd thing was, that with the enemy only a short distance away across the desert, he still could not guarantee himself this simple bit of satisfaction at a time when he wanted it so badly. The sense of frustration added to his burning resentment. At that moment he could cheerfully have seen the Company's position over-run, granted that it provided him with the opportunity of striking his own personal blow.

Later on, when it grew dark, he was pleased to have a bit of unexpected business crop up to distract his thoughts for a while from that staggering postcard. One of the platoon sergeants from the forward positions who had come up in a truck to draw rations and water, put his head inside the cave.

" I've brought a gun up for you to look at," he said, noting at the same time the position of the Sergeant-Major's eyebrows. Being the bearer of bad news himself, the sign was not encouraging.

" What's the matter with it ? " asked the Sergeant-Major.

" Knocked out. Got a shell on top of it. Four men wounded. I've had them taken to hospital."

The Sergeant-Major frowning heavily, took the details, and then accompanied the Platoon Sergeant outside to examine the gun. It had received a nasty knock, and two feed-blocks were burned by the fire caused by the exploding shell. The Platoon Sergeant had also brought along several spare parts that had been damaged.

" All right," said the Sergeant-Major, when he had finished his examination. " I'll get you another gun and equipment from the Q.M.S., and have it sent along. Much sign of life up there to-day ? "

" Usual shelling. Not more than we've been having," replied the Platoon Sergeant, mounting his truck to depart. " Very sorry to hear of your bad knock."

The Sergeant-Major acknowledged his sympathy with a curt nod, and he drove back to the forward positions with the information that he had never seen the C.S.M. in such a black mood before, but that this time he had every cause to be.

Next morning the frown on the Sergeant-Major's forehead was as pronounced as ever. Several further hours of brooding over the massacre of his relatives had only fomented his desire for immediate personal retaliation. And side by side with this had increased the acute exasperation at his own impotency. The dour expression on the usually cheerful face struck the Company Commander forcibly as he entered the cave shortly after nine o'clock.

" He's taking it badly," he thought. " And I can't blame him."

Aloud, he said : " Will you go up to No. 4 platoon, Sergeant-Major, and test the dial sight of that gun which was knocked out yesterday. It may be out of adjustment. They know you're coming. I've already been on the 'phone."

The Sergeant-Major mounted his truck and drove along the winding sandy track that ran parallel to the Derna road, with the escarpment on the left. The track led into a big wadi, liberally furnished with boulders of all shapes and sizes, some as big as small rocks. The final approach to the gun positions was up the side of the wadi, and this being too steep for the truck, he left it behind with the driver to await his return and continued the journey on foot. Away on the right he could hear the echoes of distant shelling, but everything seemed quiet enough in his own area.

Platoon H.Q. was sandbagged up on the ledges of the wadi, just below the lip. When the Sergeant-Major arrived the platoon commander shouted for the No. 4 platoon sergeant to take him up to the position on the crest of the wadi. A gun, with the doubtful dial sight lying beside it, was awaiting the Sergeant-Major just in the rear of the gun position. With the platoon sergeant standing-by he speedily set to work. First he set the gun on a horizontal plane by means of three dial sights which they knew were accurate. Then he fixed on the gun the dial sight which was to be tested, and watched the little air bubble floating in the oil come to rest.

" Well, I'm damned," exclaimed the platoon sergeant.

" Only ten minutes out," announced the Sergeant-Major. " I'm very surprised it's so little considering the gun got such a smack."

" Same here," said the platoon sergeant. " After that wallop, I thought it had gone for good. Just shows how much they can stand up to."

The Sergeant-Major affixed a couple of washers at the side and saw the air-bubble float central.

" That's O.K. now," he said, and proceeded to check up all the stores that had suffered in the shell explosion, so that he could make replacements as soon as possible. While so engaged the platoon commander walked across to them.

" Now the Sergeant-Major's here, better get him to test that other gun," he said.

" What's the matter with it, sir ? " asked the Sergeant-Major.

" Don't know. I suspect something wrong with the mechanism. Try a few rounds with it."

" Where shall I fire it, sir ? "

" Across the wadi, if you like."

" I want to be sure I don't hit any of our own troops," said the Sergeant-Major, dubiously.

The platoon commander, glancing at his contracted eyebrows, seemed suddenly to recollect a little matter he had overlooked.

" I was very sorry to hear about your bad news, Sergeant-Major," he said. " Don't let it get you down."

Get him down ! . . . The Sergeant-Major felt like laughing derisively. That wasn't the thing he felt oppressing him. At least not the chief thing. What filled his heart with a smouldering fury was his inability to hit back himself straight away on behalf of his dead and injured folk back in England. If he could only do that he wouldn't care a damn what happened to himself. His wife in hospital . . . and seven others dead . . . and he couldn't even begin working off the score. . . .

Suddenly the idea seized him, almost before the platoon officer had finished speaking. It wouldn't be all he could have desired. But it would be some satisfaction, a bit to go on with.

"What about firing at the enemy, sir?" he said. "Might as well test out on them. Where did you last see any movement?"

The platoon commander pointed across the desert towards the Water Tower.

"Half a mile to the right of the Tower," he said. "There were distinct signs of activity early this morning. Looked as though they'd brought up some motorised infantry during the night. I wouldn't be surprised if they put in an attack later on. Perhaps to-morrow. That's one reason I want to be sure that gun's in good fighting trim."

"I don't like the sound of this idea much," said the platoon sergeant gloomily, when the officer had departed.

"What idea?" snapped the Sergeant-Major.

"Firing on the Water Tower. I know what that'll mean."

"What?"

"You'll bring down artillery fire at once. It's always the case. The slightest sign, they start sending the stuff over. I'm telling you because I know. It makes the position bloody uncomfortable. What's wrong with firing over the wadi?"

The Sergeant-Major was not so easily to be diverted from his project. In a different frame of mind he would have readily recognised the soundness of the platoon sergeant's argument. But at present his one and only consideration was to send his personal message straight to the heart of the enemy.

"You heard me say just now I didn't want to chance hitting any of our own troops," he said impatiently.

" Apart from the wadi, there's no other place except firing at the enemy. Besides, I shan't be giving anything away. You've had some already, so they know you're here."

" Yes, we've had some. That's why I don't want any more if I can avoid it," grumbled the platoon sergeant.

" In any case, you're moving into alternative positions to-morrow," said the Sergeant-Major.

" To-morrow isn't now," observed the other gloomily. " And they come over as quickly as that. Mark my words."

" All right, then," said the Sergeant-Major, irritated by the obstruction to his cherished desire. " I'll go up there on the right. . . . On that rising ground. Will that satisfy you ? "

" I can't see what's wrong with the wadi," replied the platoon sergeant unenthusiastically. But he knew from the black look on the Sergeant-Major's face that further protest was useless.

He summoned a couple of men to help carry the gun, tripod, condenser can and ammunition to the spot the Sergeant-Major had indicated, which was about two hundred yards from the gun position. They moved cautiously up the side of the slope and mounted the gun behind cover. The Sergeant-Major himself loaded it with a belt of two hundred and fifty. Feeling that it was his little show alone, and that he did not want anyone else involved in the consequences, he ordered the two gunners to retire for safety farther down the wadi.

" You'd better go, too," he said to the platoon sergeant.

But the platoon sergeant, though liking the business not at all, and filled with the gloomiest anticipations, preferred to stay. He crouched down disconsolately beside the Sergeant-Major, who sat on the ground behind the gun with his back supported by a boulder, and awaited the worst.

The Sergeant-Major, taking his time, carefully laid his sights on the spot to the right of the Water Tower where the enemy had last been seen. He had no real target, but thinking of his injured wife and his seven dead relatives as he looked along the sights, he had a confident hope that by the time he had got rid of his two hundred and fifty rounds he would have paid off some of that debt. And at the moment that was all that mattered to him. Just as he was about to press the thumb-piece the platoon sergeant made a last attempt.

"I warn you," he said. "The shells will come on top of us within three minutes."

"I'll chance that," shouted the Sergeant-Major as the gun rattled off its first burst of twenty-five in the direction of the Water Tower. Another burst followed immediately.

"Side plates of this gun are slightly buckled," commented the Sergeant-Major, who had not forgotten, while engaged on his own private affair, to take notice of how the gun behaved.

The platoon sergeant hoped that now the fault had been discovered the Sergeant-Major would be content.

"Better pack up now," he urged.

"I'm staying till I've finished," announced the Sergeant-Major, pressing the thumb-piece once more.

As he did so a shell screamed through the air and burst with a shattering explosion a hundred and fifty yards in front of the gun.

"There you are. . . . Didn't I tell you so? . . ." groaned the platoon sergeant.

But the Sergeant-Major was now beyond any expostulations or sense of personal danger. He was thinking of nothing but all those killed and wounded belonging to him back in England. The machine-gun continued firing with only the shortest breaks between the bursts.

Another shell arrived. This one screamed over their heads and burst a hundred yards behind them.

"For Christ's sake let's go," yelled the platoon sergeant. "They've made a bracket. The next will land on top of us."

This time the Sergeant-Major was ready to quit. He had emptied his belt, and already felt a bit better for it. The men were called up from the wadi to collect the kit and take it down the slope, while the other two hurriedly dismounted the gun. The Sergeant-Major was as willing now as the platoon sergeant to recognise that every second mattered. He took the gun himself, and with his companion carrying the tripod, they hastened from the spot together.

They hadn't proceeded more than fifteen yards when the shell arrived. A common impulse caused them both to turn their heads to watch. They saw the shell drop dead on the spot where they had been sitting only a few moments before. Next instant a chunk of the boulder which had supported the Sergeant-Major's back whizzed between them, so close that they felt the draught. In that instant, as they stood spellbound expecting the explosion, the Sergeant-Major was aware of the platoon sergeant's gaze turned reproachfully on him, and of himself thinking that he didn't mind what his own packet would be, but that it would be hard luck on the sergeant.

And then he was surprised to find himself still thinking. . . . And then he realised the shell hadn't burst. . . . And then they were scurrying down the slope again, laughing aloud.

" By God, a dud ! " shouted the platoon sergeant excitedly. " Right on top of us—and a dud ! That's *your* luck, Sergeant-Major. That sort never comes my way."

" All I hope is I've been as lucky at the other end," replied the Sergeant-Major fervently.

On his way back to H.Q. he felt like a man who has had an abscess lanced. The sore was still there, but it wasn't throbbing so much. He thought of that two hundred and fifty rounds with satisfaction. At any rate, it was a bit on account.

" The line of direction was all right, or they wouldn't have been so prompt to reply. And it surely was my lucky day. And seven isn't many to expect out of a full belt. So who knows ? " he argued optimistically.

The Quartermaster was alone in the cave when the Sergeant-Major entered. He noticed at once that the eyebrows had assumed their usual position.

" About that tin of beer ? " exclaimed the Sergeant-Major briskly.

" What tin ? " inquired the Quartermaster.

" The one you offered me last night. I feel like a drink."

" So did I," said the Quartermaster. " Last night."

IX—THROUGH HAPPY VALLEY

THE driver brought the 15-cwt. truck to a sharp stop where the narrow, precipitous track came to a sudden end half-way down the wadi.

Almost before the vehicle halted the two tank corporals chucked out their kit-bags and alighted beside them. There ensued a few moments silence while all three men gazed for the first time upon Happy Valley. The driver was the first to speak. He grinned pleasantly from one to the other of his companions.

" Blokes, you're jammy," he said enviously.

The two corporals, busy absorbing the details of their surroundings, just nodded frank acquiescence.

It is usually in the spirit of savage irony that the British soldier on active service applies his versatility to the gentle art of impromptu nomenclature. " The Ritz," for instance, will denote some ten-by-six dug-out, sodden or blistering according to the season, where the greatest luxury obtainable is to snatch an hour's sleep without being awakened by rats running over your face. Likewise, " Bond Street " is as likely as not to be a couple of hundred yards of very unhealthy track, where the presents so lavishly proffered to the stroller are cast in metals other than gold, platinum, or silver ; and in unfriendly shapes, such as machine-gun bullets, shell splinters, and bombs from aeroplanes.

But with Happy Valley it was different. The sentimental spirit, not the sardonic, had presided over its christening. The three men had heard a lot about this place and now, at the moment of actually beholding it, each of them considered that the name fitted it like a glove. Happy Valley fulfilled all their expectations, although it was only a deep, wide, stony wadi leading to the beach on the western side of beleaguered Tobruk. Heavy guns were roaring incessantly. Enemy shells exploded in a continuous thunder as they dropped close at hand on top of the escarpment to the left of the wadi, and threatened every moment to drop right into it. But these ominous portents failed to destroy the illusion. To the three new-comers, as to many others during those grim days at Tobruk, Happy Valley remained Happy Valley in face of all the disabilities by virtue of a certain wooden hut built in its rocky sides and designated : TRANSIT OFFICE. For Transit Office meant WAY OUT. . . . Way out to good old England eventually if you were one of the lucky ones. In any case, it meant good-bye to all the dangers, boredom, thirst, hunger, hardships and miseries of the siege.

The two tank corporals were in a proper frame of mind to appreciate all that Happy Valley implied. They had endured the rigours of the siege since the commencement, not to mention a bellyful of fighting. Now, after many months, they were being evacuated. They did not pretend to regret it. For the time being both felt choked up to the neck with Tobruk. Vic, the shorter of the two corporals, had been recommended for a commission and was going home to join an Officer Cadets Training Unit. His companion, Johnny, a powerfully-built fellow, with a broad, impassive countenance, was being evacuated on compassionate grounds, owing to the serious illness of his wife. It was doubtful if he would reach home in time to see her alive. All the same, he felt lucky to be getting out of Tobruk.

The driver, who would soon be returning in the empty truck to where the Tank squadron lay dispersed on the outer defences, continued to regard the pair with un-concealed envy.

" Don't I wish I was you blokes," he said fervently. " Unless I get knocked off I'm here for the bloody duration. My wife's as tough as a rhinoceros. An' Gawd help England if it ever comes to having to send me on O.C.T.U."

He feasted his eyes on the clump of date palms, surrounded by a patch of green grass, that grew picturesquely, and surprisingly enough, in the flat trough of the wadi.

" I call that pretty," he said with loving appreciation. " First trees I've set eyes on since we got shut in. Barring the old fig tree up on the escarpment near the wire. I did go up to have a look at that once. They told me it was the only tree around Tobruk. An' I like seeing all the sights. I didn't stay long, give you my word. The Jerries had a machine-gun trained on it."

A mare with a foal in attendance wandered through the clump of date palms and commenced cropping the grass in the bright October afternoon sunshine, as tranquilly as if no such thing as war and its horrors existed.

" Well, well . . ." commented the driver, fascinated. " What do you say to that ? Makes me think of home. A bloke told me about a mare having dropped a foal during a big air do. That's it, I suppose. Good luck to the old girl. . . . Anything more I can do for you boys ? Any loving messages to the squadron ? "

" Already delivered," laughed Vic. " And forgotten."

" Then what about doing something for me ? "

" Such as ? "

" You can't buy me a drink because there isn't a pub. But I won't say ' No ' to that jug of yours, Vic, empty. You know . . . a farewell present."

" Aren't you a champion old scrounger ? " exclaimed Johnnie. " That's Vic's mascot."

" Well, now I've brought you here its job's over, isn't it ? What use is a mascot to a bloke who hasn't got to stop in Tobruk ? An' what use is a jug with a lid on to keep out the desert, when you'll be at sea within an hour or two ? What d'you say, Vic ? "

" It's yours," said the corporal good naturedly.

He stopped and cut the string attaching a small metal jug, equipped with a hinged lid, to the neck of his kit-bag.

" The art of keeping out the sand is to take quick mouthfuls and slap the lid down before you remove the jug from your lips," he explained. " Don't try a long drink. It needs practice."

" I'll learn it," the driver assured him. " Before I've finished I'll make this jug do its proper stuff in a dust-storm. Thanks, Vic."

He received the gift from the corporal like the treasure it was. A faint pang of regret seized Vic as he handed the jug over. It had been his constant companion throughout the campaign. True, in a way, he had come to regard it as a mascot. But its practical utility was the thing that endeared it to him most. That jug with a lid had kept bushels of grit out of his gullet. He didn't believe there was another like it in the whole Division. It had been the envy of half the squadron, and ever since leaving Alexandria he had had to guard it vigilantly against " borrowers." The fact that he was now parting with it of his own free-will brought home to him more strongly than anything else the great change that had taken place in his circumstances. He was actually leaving the desert. Actually going somewhere where a drink would mean something more than a mouthful of wet grit. That thought alone was enough to make a fellow joyful. Nevertheless, he felt a shade sad as he watched the driver deposit his trusty old friend in the back of the truck.

" I'll be moving now," said the driver. " If I stay looking at them trees much longer I won't want to go back. Good luck, boys. Hope you'll find the missis sitting up and telling off the doctor, corporal."

The engine roared and the truck began to back gratingly up the slope. Before passing out of earshot the driver thrust a grinning face from the side and yelled his last farewell :

" You jammy bastards ! "

The two corporals laughed contentedly.

" I'm not quarrelling with that," said Vic as the truck disappeared. " Only hope he's right. Come on. Let's discover this Transit Office."

Slinging their kit-bags, they made their way down to the bottom of the wadi. Scattered about here and there in small groups were two or three-score men who had already arrived for evacuation. Others were still drifting in from various units. The men lounged about in the shade of the small rocks, and under the date palms dozing, smoking, and chatting in low voices, almost as if afraid of betraying their presence to the enemy. They had nothing to do now but await the moment of embarkation and hope that there would be no last-minute upset.

A couple of lean, hairy, and battle-stained Australians directed the two corporals to the wooden hut on the side of the wadi. Here they gave their names to the Transit Officer and each produced his authority to leave. It was a sheet of paper with the man's number, name, and rank typed at the top, and read :

" The above-mentioned N.C.O. has been detailed to report to Officer I.C. Transit Camp for embarkation on first available vessel to enable him to report to Abassia Barracks, Cairo, on the 15th inst."

" All right," said the Transit Officer after examining the dockets.

" Any instructions, sir ? " asked Vic.

" Yes. When you get down to the harbour see you've got both arms free. And put on plimsolls."

" Haven't got any."

" Well, pull a pair of socks over your boots. Save you from slipping on the wet jetty and decks."

" Any more ? "

" No ; just hang around till you're called for."

" When's that likely to be ? "

"Not before dark. Meanwhile, don't group thickly, and keep under cover as much as possible. It's wonderful what Jerry sees from the air."

The two corporals sauntered away to the shade of the date palms. It was after four in the afternoon and the sun was blazing. Though they still wore their pull-over and great-coats, they were little conscious of the warmth. The excitement engendered by their coming exit from Tobruk was all the heat they felt. And they found that good.

They squatted near a group of four infantrymen engaged in a desultory conversation around the only topic of vital interest to the occupants of the wadi, namely, their chances of making a good get-away that night. Their great fear was that an enemy air raid might come along and upset embarkation arrangements. For a while the two corporals listened casually without joining in the talk, until one of the speakers happened to remark :

"Wonder if Bardia Bill will have something to say to us to-night."

The mention of this celebrated name diverted Johnny's attention from the clusters of hard green dates that hung like bunches of grapes on the palms overhead.

"Bardia Bill," he exclaimed in surprise. "How does he come into the picture ? "

"Shells the harbour most nights," said the infantry-man. "Jerry knows there's something doing here after dark. Men going out and supplies coming in. I bet by now that gun's got the exact range."

"And a pretty long one, too," laughed Vic sceptically. "Why, Bardia is over fifty miles away."

"All right, clever bloke. But they've brought the gun up the coast so it can command the harbour. Wait till to-night. You'll see if I know what I'm talking about."

"I went and had a look at that gun after we mopped up Bardia," said Johnny. "A hell of a weapon, on a sort of platform mounting. While we were waiting outside to put in the attack you could recognise old Bill's boom above all the barrage. Must have been a sixteen-inch shell. I wouldn't like to have got in its way. I wonder whether my name's still on it."

" What d'you mean ? " said the infantryman, staring at him.

" I scratched my name on Old Bill. Just under the breech, with a knife," Johnny explained.

" What made you do that ? "

" Just to let him know I'd called. I didn't have a visiting card," Johnny laughed.

The infantryman regarded him gloomily for a few moments.

" Glad you told me, corporal," he said. " I'll give you a wide berth when we get down to the harbour."

Johnny's smile faded and his face became wooden and hostile.

" Meaning just what ? " he asked.

" Well, a bloke what writes his name like that on a gun is to my mind asking for trouble," said the infantryman slowly. " Like inviting Bardia Bill to return your call. And I don't want to be around when it happens."

Johnny gazed at him incredulously.

" That's one I've never heard before," he exclaimed. " What bloody rubbish. . . . Were you one of those newspaper astrologers ? "

Vic and the other soldiers began to laugh.

" Can't you see he's kidding you ? " they said.

" No, I ain't," the infantryman insisted, obstinately. " You can laugh if you like. But funny things happen. I've seen some of 'em out here. You look after yourself to-night, corporal, if Bardia Bill gets on the job."

" Bardia Bill ! . . ." echoed one of his companions scornfully, spitting the end of a cigarette from his lips. " There never was any such gun. It's a myth. I'll tell you what Bardia Bill was. It was a battery of four hundred-and-fives planted in that wadi on the south-east of the town. I saw them myself."

"Well, you don't know nothing about it," interposed another of the group. "Bardia Bill was really two pairs of fourteen-inch naval guns mounted on Bardia headland."

"What about the gun I saw?" Johnny objected.

"One of them naval guns, I expect."

"No, it wasn't. It was down on the south defences, nowhere near Bardia headland."

Further development of the argument was cut short by someone hammering on a 60-pounder shell-case outside the big shed that was the cookhouse. The time-honoured chant echoed through the wadi :

"Come and get it . . ."

All over the wadi men scrambled to their feet and made for the cookhouse, where the three cooks had prepared the final meal before embarkation. Instinctively they observed the precautions against bunching, despite the keenness of their appetites. They queued up at the cookhouse a dozen at a time. And as one queue was dealt with, another formed. It was past five o'clock, and by now fully two hundred men had assembled in the wadi, all to be evacuated for various reasons. Almost every unit had its representative. There were infantry, Tank men, machine-gunners, artillery, Signals, R.A.M.C.—British and Australian—who had been in Tobruk since the siege started, and Poles belonging to the relieving force that had been pushed in from the sea later. The same feeling of suppressed excitement possessed all of them. The same longing to get away for a spell from the monotony of the siege and the baked, featureless desert. The same undercurrent of anxiety that something might happen, even now at the eleventh hour, to cancel their departure.

The two corporals queued up with the others at the cookhouse, holding out their mugs for a helping of bully-beef stew. Having consumed this, they mopped out the mugs with dirty handkerchiefs and tailed on to another queue for tea and hard-tack biscuits.

Towards six o'clock the sun went down and the wadi

was shrouded in a sudden darkness. Now the men collected in small bunches within earshot of the Transit Hut, whence would eventually come the call that meant so much to them. There wasn't the glimmer of a light anywhere. Those who smoked, lit their cigarettes carefully under greatcoats, and covered them with the palm of the hand. No one needed to be informed of the urgency of these precautions. Each man knew that in the event of an air-raid the chances of being evacuated that night would be infinitesimal. The little groups of men waited patiently in the darkness, listening to the roar of the big guns, British and enemy, that never ceased. The enemy shells continued to fall on the top of the escarpment, as they had been doing all the afternoon. In the darkness the explosions sounded so close that it was easy to imagine some of the shells were dropping in the wadi itself. As the minutes passed the tenseness among the men increased. There was little conversation. Everyone was too absorbed in his own thoughts. What fragmentary talk did take place still revolved round the prospects of an air raid. It was uppermost in everybody's mind. Out of the pitch-black night, a few yards from where the two corporals squatted on the ground alone, came a mutter from an invisible inquirer :

" Any moon to-night ? "

" No . . ." said another voice.

" Yes . . ." said another.

" What time does it get up ? . . ."

The information did not seem to be forthcoming.

" Up late," volunteered Vic, into the darkness. " It's on the wane."

" Thanks," muttered the first voice. " How much longer have we got to wait here for the bloody Navy ? Don't they know we're here ? "

Somebody burst into a laugh that sounded strange and out-of-place in the general tension.

" Vic," whispered Johnny suddenly, " I'd like to have given that bloke a punch on the jaw, this afternoon."

" What bloke ? "

" That foot-slogger who said he'd give me a wide berth down at the harbour."

" Forget it, boy. He's bats. . . . Johnny, you're not telling me you believe there's anything in that Bardia Bill bullsh ? " Vic asked, sitting up in astonishment.

" I don't believe it, Vic," Johnny hastened to say. " But when I think about that bloke, it makes me mad. I'm in a pretty big hurry to get to England, Vic. You know how it is with my wife. I've got so far, and then along comes this fortune-telling bastard and more than hints. . . ."

" And you're mug enough to let that half-wit plant a fool idea in your mind," interrupted Vic, impatiently. " And you're a bigger mug still to start brooding on it. What's come over you, Johnny ? Gone bomb-happy ? "

" My nerve's all right," said Johnny sulkily. " You don't understand, Vic. I'm not afraid of anything. I just feel it would be a comic turn-up if I didn't get away, after all."

" Through the kind offices of Bardia Bill," added Vic, remorselessly. " That's what you're feeling. Listen, prize mug. You may not get away, I may not get away, and none of us may get away. And if we don't it'll be because of the Heinkels, not Bardia Bill. If you want to get a flap up, get a flap about something that's real. Then I'll be interested, and maybe join you."

After this cold douche, Johnny lapsed into an aggrieved silence, which Vic, who felt annoyed with his companion for being fool enough to give a moment's thought to Bardia Bill, made no effort to dispel. For another quarter of an hour they remained without speaking, just conscious in the impenetrable darkness of one another's presence.

Suddenly there was a perceptible stir in the wadi, as though a slight breeze had passed through.

" Hullo, something's doing," said Vic, and they both scrambled to their feet.

A man had appeared at the door of the Transit Office. He began to call out names, pausing between each. As the names were shouted, men detached themselves one by one from the dark groups and made their way to the hut. When twenty had been collected, the party was put in charge of the senior officer, or N.C.O., and, led by a guide, disappeared up the black face of the wadi as though suddenly swallowed up. After they had departed, another twenty names were called.

While the third batch was being collected, Vic heard his name shouted. As it happened, he was the last of that twenty.

" See you down at the harbour, Johnny," he said, slapping him on the shoulder.

" I'll be there," replied Johnny.

When Vic reached the Transit Hut the guide was ready to start them on their journey. In single file, in the pitch darkness, the party began to scramble up a steep, rocky goat-track, that zig-zagged all the way, so that it was extremely difficult to keep any sense of direction. Unable to see a yard in front of them, men crashed blindly into boulders and tripped over tufts of camel thorn. The air was full of the sound of muffled curses, and the clatter of falling rifles as their owners pitched head-foremost on to the low rocks. Sometimes the track shot up almost perpendicularly, and the men had to dig in their toes and claw with their finger-nails to keep them from tumbling backwards. Even on the moderate gradients it was bad enough. Vic, like most of the others, eventually discovered that the surest method of progress was to grope forward on the ground on all fours, just following the sound made by the man in front of him. He was last in the file, and dread of losing touch with the others stimulated him to fresh exertions, although his heart was pounding against his ribs before the climb was half over.

Over twenty minutes had elapsed after leaving the hut when the party finally emerged on the top of the escarpment, torn, bleeding, panting and exhausted. They came out on the side facing the south-east, and across on their right the night horizon was lit with the flashes

of the heavy guns firing over the desert.   From areas
to the south came the incessant rattle of the enemy's
Breda guns, a sure sign, Vic knew, that our patrols were
busy.   He recalled, too, that the tanks would be going
out that night.   He listened for the familiar crack of
the two-pounders, but could not hear anything.   One
minute he was sorry he was missing the fun with the
Squadron.   The next he was perfectly contented to be
shaking the dust of Tobruk off his heels.   " I'll bet in a
couple of days I'll be wishing I was back," he thought,
as his mind turned to all the good companionship he was
leaving behind.   Nevertheless, it was a great relief to
him to discover, when he thrust his head over the top
of the escarpment, that there were no strings of flaming
onions enlivening the black vault of the sky.   No sign
yet of any air raid. . . .

Several lorries were waiting on the ridge.   " Get a
move on. . . . Jump in . . ." someone ordered.   The
twenty men clambered into an empty vehicle at the tail
of two others that had already received their consign-
ments.   Now followed a wait which seemed interminable,
while the remaining parties were guided up the perilous
goat-track.   When all the vehicles were full they slowly
moved off, one behind the other, bound for the harbour.
The journey down proved as fearsome a thing as the
climb up. In the pitch darkness the lorries had the
utmost difficulty in keeping to the narrow track.   They
wandered all over the place, sometimes crashing into
one another, sometimes losing touch completely.   The
soldiers, impatient to reach the harbour once they had
started, fumed at these delays.   Angry voices shouted
into the darkness.

" Doesn't the bloody fool know his way ? . . ."
" Ain't he got eyes in his head ! . . ."
" We going to be here all night ? . . ."

None of the critics seemed to take into account the
fact that he himself could hardly see an inch before his
nose.   Once Vic's lorry got lost entirely and the men
had to dismount and push it back on to the path again,

amid fearful execrations from all those held up behind.
There was another peril, too, that kept their progress
slow. The track was deeply pitted with shell craters,
and very often a vehicle lurched into one and almost
toppled over. When this happened the occupants had
to jump out and hoist it upright again.

At last, after a nightmare descent, they came in sight
of the broken, white walls of the flat-roofed Italian
houses at the outskirts of the town. They rumbled on
past the Sciola Mussolini, and down the road till they
reached the Detention Barracks near the gates of the
town. Here they encountered an unexpected barrage
from the defaulters within, who, recognising the sound
of the vehicles, expressed their opinion of those about
to be evacuated in derisive cat-calls and obscene shouts.
The occupants of the lorries preserved silence, not for
lack of ammunition, but because their whole attention
was concentrated on the harbour beyond. To them the
moment was too serious a one for back-chat. The
vehicles proceeded down the road to Hell Fire Corner,
a favourite target for enemy guns during the day time.
Here, where the road twisted down to the harbour, the
lorries pulled up. The men alighted and, in accordance
with the instructions from the Transit Officer, began to
free their arms from encumbrances and to put on plimsolls
or pull socks over their boots.

Suddenly, not far away, a gong sounded loud and
menacingly.

" Air Raid . . ." bellowed a Voice of Authority from
the darkness.

" Blast and blast . . ." Vic muttered to himself, dis-
gustedly. " Just what I've been expecting. . . . No
embarkation to-night."

The men scattered to take cover and in a moment or
two the street was silent and deserted. Ten minutes
passed. Then the Voice of Authority, that seemed to
know everything, bellowed again :

" All clear . . ."

With low exclamations of relief the men scurried back

from their holes like reprieved rabbits, and gathered again on the tarmac road round the vehicles. Those who had been separated from their friends began to shout out names, and among them Vic recognised Johnny's voice :

" Vic, where are you ? . . . Vic . . ."

" Over here, Johnny. . . . This way, Johnny . . ." he continued shouting back.

In a few seconds Johnny materialised from the black night.

" Thought you were lost, Vic. I've been looking everywhere for you."

" Sure you didn't think I was giving you a wide berth ? " said Vic, half-jokingly.

" I ran into that infantry bloke just now," muttered Johnny. " Soon as he saw who it was he sheered off as if I was poison."

" My God. . . . Have you still got that on the brain ? " cried Vic. " How could you tell it was him in the dark ? You couldn't see his face. Nor could he see yours. Besides, suppose it was him ? What then ? "

A voice cut short their conversation.

" Fall in. . . . All this way. . . ."

They marched in order down to the quay, tripping in the darkness over the loose telephone wires that lay across the road. The harbour was black and silent, except for the sound of the little waves lapping against the side of the quay. Silhouettes of wrecked vessels stuck up out of the water like monstrous spectres, the half-sunken Italian cruiser *San Giorgio* being the most conspicuous.

A couple of small flat-bottomed barges were tied alongside the jetty, each with a high, square prow, and fitted with a donkey-engine aft. Into these the men tumbled. The first barge chugged off into the dark harbour. The second, in which were Vic and Johnny, refused to budge. After a lot of confusion it was discovered that the barge was aground forward. Orders were given for the men to disembark. They gathered on the quayside, chafing at the delay. Suddenly the barge started to move, and, fearful of being left behind, the entire crowd of them took flying leaps in the darkness and landed on top of one another in the bottom of the vessel. Impatient shouts went up to " Cast Off," the ropes were untied, and the barge slowly nosed its way out into the centre of the harbour in search of the destroyer that was supposed to have crept in after nightfall to take the men off. But no destroyer could be found. The two barges chugged through the black waters heading in turn for everything that loomed up ahead. In this way they explored most of the wrecks in the harbour. But the much-desired destroyer eluded them. Nearly half an hour was spent in criss-crossing the harbour without result. By this time the temper of the troops began to shorten appreciably.

" What the hell are they playing at ? . . ."

" We ain't out for a nice sail round the harbour . . ."

" Fine bloody mess-up . . ."

A continual fire of sarcasm was directed at those navigating the barges.

At last they drew near the quay once more. A voice from one of the barges shouted :

" Can't find her."

" Come back and tie up," came an order from the quay.

It was a bitter disappointment to the men on board, who now believed that some hitch in the arrangements had occurred to prevent their evacuation at the very last moment. The sarcasm and the grumblings died down, giving place to a gloomy silence.

Suddenly, away across the harbour eastwards, on the far coast, appeared a big orange-green flash, followed by a dull boom.

Vic felt Johnny grip his arm tightly, and heard him exclaim :

" Bardia Bill . . ."

Almost immediately the shell whined overhead. It burst with a terrific explosion on the edge of the quay not far away, but without doing any injury to the barges.

"Count thirty from the time you see the flash, and if you can count another two after you hear the report, you'll know you're alive, Johnny," said Vic.

They stared across the harbour and saw the next flash appear, just as the barges were tying up. This time the shell burst away to the left on the land side. After this the shells began to drop into the water all round them. It became very evident that the big gun was methodically searching the harbour. The surface of the water was churned up into quite respectable waves and the men could feel the barges vibrating under their feet after each explosion. Expecting every moment to be hurled into the water, they began loosening their kit, ready to make a swim for it.

"Your infantry bloke was right about one thing, Johnny," remarked Vic. "That gun's got the range all right."

There was no reply from Johnny. Since the shelling first started he had not uttered a word. He stood, still gripping Vic's arm, staring in a rather spellbound way at the distant coast where sprang the orange-green flashes.

"You still being a blasted fool?" said Vic, derisively.

About a dozen shells fell altogether. Then came a long pause.

"Look's as though the strafe's over for to-night," observed Vic. "You can come out of your trance, Johnny."

Once again the barges cast off and nosed out into the black harbour. Hardly had they started when, to everybody's surprise, there was another dull boom away on the eastern headland, and another shell whined above them. It was the big gun's farewell. The last shot. It burst in the water less than a hundred yards from the barges, hurling up a fountain of spray.

With the roar of the explosion still deafening him, Johnny suddenly felt Vic stagger against him and collapse on the bottom of the barge. For a moment or two he stared down at the heap at his feet, unable to comprehend what had happened. A voice shouted:

" Man down here. . . ."

From the front of the barge someone in authority shouted back :

" Is he badly hit ? . . . Can he go on ? . . ."

As Johnny bent down Vic clutched his arm and struggled to his feet, leaning heavily on his companion.

" You hit, Vic ? " Johnny asked, anxiously.

" Yes," whispered Vic.

" Where's it got you ? "

" In the chest, I think."

" Bad ? "

" I don't feel so good," said Vic, in a low tone. He gripped the other's arm tighter to support himself. " Johnny," he whispered urgently, " I'm like you. I want to go on. . . . Don't let them put me ashore. . . ."

The voice from the front of the barge shouted again :

" Can that man go on ? . . ."

" O.K.," Johnny yelled back. " Bloke slipped over."

" Pore little feller ! " drawled some humorist, and raised a laugh.

The barge continued on its way. This time it appeared to be following new instructions. Dodging the half-submerged wrecks it headed for the opposite coast, and in a short while there loomed out of the darkness the shape of a warship. As the barge drew alongside a voice from the deck above shouted :

" What have you got there ? "

" Troops."

" Then take the bloody things away," was the facetious reply.

From the bottom of the barge a big wooden ladder with two-foot rungs was hoisted, not without much difficulty, against the side of the ship and lashed to the rail at the top. The eager troops swarmed up it.

" We've made it, Vic," said Johnny excitedly, still half-supporting the wounded man. " You'll be all right once you get up the ladder."

" Can't do it," replied Vic faintly.

" You've got to, Vic. Even if I have to push you up.

Don't you worry. I'll be behind to hold you if you stumble. But for God's sake, try," whispered Johnny fiercely.

He stood aside in the darkness with his arm around Vic, and allowed all the other occupants of the barge to mount the ladder first.

When the last man was beginning his ascent, Johnny pushed Vic on to the lowest rung of the ladder and pressed close behind him, with one hand firmly planted in the centre of his back in case he fell. By a desperate effort Vic managed to climb up a few feet. Then he stuck.

" Go on, Vic. . . . Only another step or two," Johnny encouraged him.

When he found that Vic still remained motionless he stretched up and lifted the leaden feet one by one to the next rung of the ladder, at the same time hoisting Vic up from the rear.

" Come on, soldier," shouted the impatient sailor at the top of the ladder. " Don't hold up the war."

Sweating and panting under his exertions, Johnny gradually edged Vic upwards till they half-fell over the ship's rail on to the deck.

" Ham an' eggs and coffee in the mess-deck below," the sailor informed them. " Looks like that bloke can do with some."

Suddenly Vic slipped heavily from the support of Johnny's arm and crumpled up on the deck. When Johnny knelt down and raised his head, Vic opened his eyes slowly. His lips parted in a faint smile.

" Johnny," he murmured with difficulty, " Bardia Bill . . . can't read . . . made a mistake in the name. . . ."

Then his eyes closed again.

" What's the matter with him ? " asked the sailor.

Johnny stood up.

" I think he's dead," he said slowly.

X—Sitting Target

"Driver . . . left . . . left . . . right," slowly chanted the tank sergeant down the microphone, keeping his eye glued to the ground before him as it swam into view in his periscope.

"Right. . . ."

And then, almost immediately, it was : " Left . . . left . . ." again. As it had been, in fact, times out of all proportion during the Matilda II's recent progress.

Between the two orders the sergeant squeezed in a curt monosyllable, very expressive of his accumulated wrathful frustration. At this rate he would soon be right out of touch with the squadron.

The tank the sergeant commanded was on the extreme left of the squadron. At first everything had gone swimmingly. They had crashed through the outer defences of the town just after dawn. During the night the sappers with their Bangalore torpedoes had blasted wide passages through the barbed wire, and driven safe tracks through the minefields beyond. All the tanks had to do was to sail through, mopping up the enemy gun-posts as they reached them. It was pie—not forgetting the ferocious barrage the enemy's big artillery hidden away in the distant wadis was putting down.

After traversing nice clean ground for some time, the sergeant suddenly discovered himself deep in an un-suspected minefield. The light was growing stronger now, and he began to thread his way through, slowly and carefully, seizing every opportunity to veer towards the right, in the direction of the remainder of the squadron. But the mines weren't having any. They persisted in diverting his course constantly to the left. The gap between himself and the squadron widened. Already they had passed out of sight. He was on his lonesome.

"Left . . ." he ordered again viciously, to avoid another suspicious-looking patch.

At the same time he began to wonder whether he wasn't being over-careful. Was he seeing mines that weren't there? . . . He'd a good mind to chance it next time. . . .

But behind a full and somewhat expressionless face the sergeant possessed a dash of imagination. And like most imaginative men, he placed great reliance on his instinct. His instinct at this moment was telling him they *were* mines. In his imagination he could even see the deadly oblong metal boxes, barely covered by the surface of the sand. Like coffins. . . .

Well, he didn't require his yet. . . .

Besides, there were too many car tracks scoring the suspected ground. They weren't there for nothing. He wasn't to be caught by that old Jerry trick.

So when the time came round again he savagely rasped out, " Left. . . ."

Hardly had he spoken when a terrific explosion sounded right on top of them, momentarily deafening the four occupants of the tank, and jolting them out of their seats. Black, acrid smoke began to pour into the tank through the ventilators and every conceivable crevice. The festoon lighting expired instantaneously, leaving them coughing and choking in darkness through which, as the smoke gradually settled, the white painted inner shell of the tank emerged like a ghostly dawn.

Half dazed by the shock, the sergeant at first thought his instinct had played him false and led him on to a mine. Then as the stench of the fumes enlightened him he shouted in the deafened ear of the loader : " Lump of H.E. . . ."

And simultaneously he became aware that the tank was behaving oddly. It seemed to lurch convulsively, half-stop, then take another heavy plunge forward.

" Driver . . . right . . ." yelled the sergeant, with his eye back at the periscope. " Right . . ." he bawled down the microphone again.

Below in the bows of the tank, with only a segment of his back visible to the sergeant, the driver wrenched

with all his might at the control stick on his right. All
that happened was that the tank made a final spasmodic
lurch in its original direction.

" Right . . ." again roared the sergeant.

This time nothing happened at all.   The tank remained
motionless, though the engine still pounded away.

" Switch off . . ." ordered the sergeant in disgust.
And immediately in the sudden silence that enveloped
the interior of the tank, they could hear more distinctly
the bursting shells of the barrage dropping round them.

Barely six seconds had elapsed since the first explosion.
For another six seconds the tank crew, breathing deeply
in the unnatural stillness within their walls, were engaged
in recovering from the shock.   The loader, a long-faced,
lugubrious-looking fellow, with wisps of a month's over-
due hair-cut sticking out from under his beret, was first
to speak.

" What have we done, Sergeant ? " he said gloomily.
" Run over a cat ? "

The sergeant's mind had already been busy with possibilities, and he had made his guess.

" That bloody shell has caught the track," he announced
to no one in particular.   " I'll have a look."

He stood up and lifted the flaps above him, intending
to climb out of the turret and inspect the nature of the
damage.   The top of his head was just on the point
of emerging, when he dropped back hastily, closing the
flaps as he did so.   Machine-gun bullets rattled on the
steel like a heavy hail.   There was a brief pause after
the first spate, and then another burst followed, and
another.   The sergeant delivered himself of a grunt to
mark his escape, and slightly loosened the swathe of
scarf round his neck.

Fifty yards behind them another heavy shell burst,
flinging up a fountain of sand and smoke.

" Not so healthy," observed the loader sadly.   " Where
do we go from here? "

The characteristic pessimism of the loader was familiar
to the sergeant.   Sometimes it made him laugh.   But

at this juncture he was not in the mood for it. He felt that the loader, in his particular lugubrious way, had expressed too closely the thoughts running in his own mind. And these he preferred not to hear aloud. The gunner remained silent. But the sergeant knew full well that he, too, shared in the swift recognition of the peculiar danger they were in. That machine-gun fire was only too explicit.

Forcibly he remembered a discussion he had once taken part in at the Tank School. They were talking about the severest ordeal that could befall a tank crew. It was decided that nothing could be worse than to be immobilised in a heavy barrage, and to be pinned down, hour after hour perhaps, expecting every minute to get the pass-out. That was more nerve-wracking even than having your tank set on fire. Because then you *had* to get out—if you could. You had no option. In any case, whatever happened was over quickly.

Listening to the rattle of machine-gun bullets against the turret, the sergeant realised grimly that they were pinned down right enough. In face of that fire there was no earthly chance of getting out to do repairs, even if the damage could be repaired. He peered through the periscope as he turned it slowly, raking minutely each sector of the ground in front as it came into vision. After a while he gave a nod of satisfaction. He had found what he wanted. There it was, about four hundred yards away on the left. He could just detect the top layer of rough stones of the machine-gun post, almost hidden from view by a low sand dune.

" Besa . . traverse left . . . left . . ." he shouted down the microphone. " Left. . . ."

The silent gunner traversed his machine-gun as ordered. When the target appeared in line with his sighting vane the Sergeant yelled : " You're on. . . . Fire ! . . ."

The sharp tat-tat-tat of the Besa was almost immediately answered by a fresh burst of fire fron the enemy post. For some time the duel continued, punctuated every now and then by the explosion of the big shells

that dropped around them with increasing frequency.
At each explosion the sergeant's impatience to silence
the machine-gun fire that held them prisoners redoubled.
He decided to try the effect of a shell or two.

" Two-pounder . . ." he shouted down the microphone.
But the rest of the order was lost in a terrific detonation
as an H.E. shell landed plump on the turret. In the
confined space of the tank it seemed to the crew that
the burst occurred right inside their own ears. A shower
of tiny particles of white-hot metal, rendered molten by the
force of the shell's impact on the turret, descended upon
them like a fiery rain, and they hurled themselves against
the far side of the turret in a desperate effort to escape.

But though the shell dented the armour it failed to
penetrate. When the fireworks ceased the three men
sorted themselves out of a heap and took a long breathing
space. They needed it, with the drums of their ears
half burst by the concussion, and their eyes still dazzled
by the startling shower-bath of white-hot sparks. Even
the taciturn gunner was moved to speech.

" Lucky that weren't a slug," he said.

" Next one may be," added the loader immediately,
with an air of gloomy conviction.

" And wouldn't you be happy if you found you were
right," the sergeant retorted in fierce sarcasm.

Once again he felt angry at hearing his own inmost
thoughts expressed. He had been trying for some time
to forget the existence of such things as solid armour-
piercing shells. They could be awkward enough even
when you were on the move. But on a sitting target,
such as they were now presenting . . .

No, the sergeant didn't like to contemplate the possibility of big slugs in the circumstances. A nasty picture
floated into his mind out of a tank battle in which he
had participated earlier in the campaign. He remembered
a German tank that had been caught " sitting " by an
armour-piercing shell. He saw again vividly the smoking
ruin, the burning bodies hanging half out of the turret
and hatch. . . .

Almost twelve months before, in the Wavell push, the sergeant had driven his tank through the Bardia defences to clear a way for the Australian infantry. He remembered the exhilarating sense of power and security that had accompanied him on that jaunt. How everything had seemed to exist as a destined target for him. The grand feeling as they rolled along that they were impregnable, with nothing to do but sweep all obstacles aside. On top of the world. . . .

And it had been the same this time, until a minute or two ago, until that damn track went. The sergeant ruefully recognised the change that had befallen since the tank came to a standstill. All that glorious sense of invulnerability and invincibility had vanished. It left him a bit cold and deflated.

" Now *we're* a target for everything that's going," he reflected grimly. " And a sitting one. . . ." He felt wide open to disaster.

In the impassive faces of the gunner and loader he seemed to trace the reflection of his own ominous thoughts. Glancing down at the driver's hunched torso in the bows, he imagined he could read the same writing there.

" Two-pounder . . . same target . . . you're on. . . . Fire ! . . ." he shouted.

The silent gunner, his brow pressed against the concussion pad, pulled the trigger beneath the gun. As he did so, a terrific thud shook them all up. An anti-tank shell had hit the armour in front of the driver's head. It was rapidly followed by three others, all crashing on practically the same spot.

" Are you all right, Danny ? " yelled the sergeant to the driver in the pause that followed.

There was no reply.

" Danny . . ." he shouted again. And there was still no response.

The sergeant, fearing the worst, edged his way with difficulty to the bow of the tank where the driver's body appeared to be sagging in its seat.

" Been hit ? " he asked, with his mouth at the back of the other's head.

" No. . . . Got a hell of a headache . . ." muttered the driver, still half dazed from the concussion.

The sergeant found expression for his relief in biting sarcasm.

" All right," he said. " I'll send nurse along at once with a couple of aspirins. . . . You're bloody lucky to have a head to ache."

He clambered back to the turret.

" For Christ's sake stop that ' ant ' ! " he shouted to the gunner. " It's giving Danny a headache."

The two-pounder continued to fire as fast as the loader could ram in the shells, the gunner peering along the sights and elevating it slightly after the first few rounds by pressing his shoulder against the leather pad on the gun-mounting. After a while the enemy post disappeared from their view in a thick cloud of dust and smoke. No more was heard for the time from the anti-tank gun or the machine-guns.

" Stop ! . . ." ordered the sergeant. " I think that's done the trick. Anyhow, we'll soon find out."

He lifted the flaps again and dropped them like a hot coal. Machine-gun bullets again pattered on the turret.

" Well, I'm damned," he said in disgust. " What d'you say to that ? . . . Knocked out one, and now there's another. That bunch came from somewhere over there on the right."

" Right or left, they hit as hard," observed the loader sadly.

The sergeant opened his lips for a smashing retort, thought better of it, and applied himself to the periscope, sweeping the ground on his right front in the hope of detecting the position of the new source of danger. He gazed long and searchingly, but could fasten on nothing definite. In the distance, over half a mile away, there rose a low sand hump which might conceal a machine-gun. But the firing had stopped. There was no sign of movement. He was baffled.

A shell from a big howitzer suddenly screamed over their heads and burst with an orange flash about fifty yards behind them. It was shortly followed by another which flung up a shower of earth, and dust and pebbles less than a hundred yards in front.

" Looks as if someone's trying to register on us," the loader remarked in a melancholy tone. " Well, as far as I can see, they can take their time."

He began to sing softly to himself :

> "Don't sign on for twenty-one,
> You'll regret it if you do. . . ."

It was a favourite ditty with the Tank Regiment, especially at their Cambrai Day celebrations on November 20th, the anniversary of the Battle of Cambrai, when the advent of a new and most potent weapon of war first became manifest to the world. Only a few weeks before, at their camp in the desert, the sergeant himself had joined lustily in the chorus. However, he was just in the mood at present to be irritated by any reminders of Cambrai Day celebrations, and especially of the fact that he himself had signed on " for twenty-one " in expectation of eventually becoming a sergeant-major. At the moment these prospects seemed so dim that he preferred to forget them. He turned fiercely on the loader.

" If you must sing, you dreary bastard," he cried, " sing something else."

The loader, who had intended nothing personal, was surprised at the vehemence of the onslaught.

" I've finished," he said, and lapsed into an aggrieved silence, while not far away another howitzer shell exploded.

The sergeant shouted to the driver :

" Your headache better, Danny ? Get out of the lower hatch and see what's happened to the track. We're pinned down up here. But I don't think they'll notice you underneath. If they do open up, we'll keep their fire down."

The driver with difficulty opened the lower escape hatch. It took him some time to scrape away the sand that had hummocked underneath. Hidden from view, he crawled flat on his stomach between the tracks, while the sergeant kept a vigilant eye on the distant sand dune, ready to open fire at the slightest sign of life. But the machine-gun remained silent. Evidently the driver's exit had passed unnoticed. He made his way to the end of the tank, and discovered the left track sagging in a big loop. Crawling round the left side, he made a quick expert survey of the damage, and then returned safely to the tank.

" What's wrong ? " asked the sergeant hurriedly.

" Couple of plates on the left track split," said the driver.

" Can we fix it ? "

" Might be able to . . . with luck. Take three of us. . . . Depends a lot on whether we can get the pin out."

" Well, for God's sake let's make a start."

" I think I can take in a bit of the slack," said the driver. He started up the engine and moved gently forward a yard or two. Then he halted.

" How are you going to get out ? " he asked the sergeant.

" I'll see to that. You get your tools."

The driver collected a spanner, hammer, drift and crowbar and crawled between the tracks again to the shelter of the left side of the tank. Within, the sergeant switched the wireless set to transmit and called up the Squadron Commander.

" Bruno Five to Bruno . . . Bruno Five to Bruno . . . I have a message for you . . . Over . . ."

Before long came the reply :

" Hello Bruno Five . . . Bruno answering . . . Pass your message . . . Bruno to Bruno Five . . . Over . . ."

The sergeant laconically stated what had happened.

" Track off . . . Under fire . . . Hope to repair later . . ."

Almost equally laconic was the Squadron-Commander's reply :

" Return to rally when repaired . . ."

" Rally " denoted the appointed rendezvous for the tanks after the action. At the present juncture, it seemed to the sergeant that the chances were pretty hot against their keeping that appointment. But there was no more to be said. He turned abruptly to the gunner and began to give him instructions.

" Understand," he concluded, " you traverse up and down that dune with short bursts as fast as you can. Spray it good and proper. That'll keep 'em down long enough for me to jump out. A minute after I've gone, do the same again for him."

He jerked his head towards the loader, at the same time saying :

" It's a risk, I know. But we've got to take a chance. If we stay here much longer, God knows what will happen."

The loader nodded in acquiescence. " I've been wanting to stretch my legs," he said.

" All right . . . Besa . . . Fire ! . . ." shouted the sergeant, without further loss of time.

The gunner traversed the short length of the sand ridge with the Besa, left to right, right to left, and back again as instructed. There was no answering burst of fire, and after the spot had been thoroughly well sprayed the sergeant flung back the flaps and leaped out of the turret to the protection of the left side of the tank. Much to his surprise, no bullets whizzed around him. He drew a deep breath of relief at finding himself intact. The driver was crouched down, waiting for him.

" Get the spare plates," said the sergeant. " Be careful not to show yourself."

The driver needed no warning. He crept along to the front of the tank, cautiously raised his arm, and loosened the bolt that fastened the two spare plates on the left side. He was returning with them when the Besa opened fire, and shortly afterwards the loader jumped from the turret. He also landed unhurt by the side of the sergeant, but this time the air sang with machine-gun bullets.

" You all right ? " asked the sergeant.

" Until I try to get back," grumbled the loader.

" One day something will happen to please you," said the sergeant. " Get hold of that spanner."

Above their heads the two-pounder suddenly cracked, much to the satisfaction of the sergeant. He knew this meant that the gunner had located the machine-gun post, and he had high hopes that it would soon be knocked out. Otherwise, he was as fully alive as the loader to the peril facing them when the time came to mount.

Having slackened off the idler wheel, the three men now settled down to their arduous task, taking it in spells to lever the broken track forward with the crowbar, and tugging on it to tauten it as much as possible. It was slow, heavy work, and after ten minutes the perspiration oozed from their faces. This in itself would not have bothered them, but the moisture attracted hordes of flies, which settled in swarms, chiefly on their upper lips, so that after a while the three of them appeared to have sprouted thick black moustaches. It was a torture they could not alleviate. With their hands occupied with the weight of the track they had few opportunities of brushing their faces free. Even so, the next second the swarm had descended on them again. They tried to get some relief by tossing their heads to and fro, like horses plagued with insects in a field on a hot summer's day. As they worked, the two-pounder continued to crack at regular intervals, and now and then a short burst of machine-gun fire spattered the other side of the tank ; from which the sergeant knew that the gunner had not yet succeeded in silencing the opposition. But he looked on the bright side. And the bright side was that they had completely knocked out the enemy post on the left. If they hadn't done so, thought the sergeant, they would have been in a bloody fine mess.

Suddenly they became aware of a new menace. A terrifying, long-drawn-out scream pierced the air.

"Cover . . . !" yelled the sergeant, with a glance at the sky. "Dive-bomber . . ."

The three of them dropped whatever they had in their hands and flung themselves under the tank. There they lay gasping for breath, while the plane dived and dived, and the ground shook with the concussion of the bombs. The reverberation of the explosions in the confined space beneath the tank half-stunned them. Occasionally the blast lifted them a few inches from the ground and bounced them heavily upon one another. Sometimes the air seemed to have been all sucked away, and they felt as if they were struggling to breathe in a vacuum. Next moment they would be breathing in draughts of powdery dust that cut like little knives.

At last, with a farewell of machine-gun fire, the plane droned away into the distance. Underneath the tank the three men collected their scattered faculties. They had no idea how long the ordeal had lasted, or whether the tank itself had been hit. They crawled out into a fog of smoke and dust and fumes that enveloped the tank. As this slowly drifted away the sergeant saw the ground all round churned up with bomb craters. The nearest was about six yards away. But the tank itself had not received any direct hit. His heart rejoiced. He knew the armour could take care of itself against flying fragments. At the same time he became aware that the two-pounder was still busy.

"Come on. . . . Let's get on with the job before the next arrives," he said briskly.

They resumed their labours on the track, finding the flies a bigger curse than the dive-bomber. Gradually they levered, dragged and coaxed till the damaged part was hanging over the idler wheel in front.

"Keep your heads down now, in case they start firing again," said the sergeant.

But his principal anxiety at this moment was whether they would be able to knock the pin holding the damaged plates out. If they couldn't, all their labours, and the risks they had run, would have been in vain. The silence that precedes a momentous event settled upon the three of them. The driver unscrewed the nut, carefully placed the drift on the head of the pin, paused a second or two for a strong, steady blow, and then struck with the hammer. The pin flew out and the broken plates dropped to the ground.

"Bloody lucky!" shouted the sergeant joyfully. "First tap. . . . We might have fooled around for half an hour and then not . . ."

He broke off abruptly. The loader was writhing on the ground, groaning in pain. Though he had heard no bullet, the sergeant concluded he must have been shot.

"Where have you got it?" he inquired, with concern.

The loader, speechless, shook his head and pointed to the track plates. A track plate is not a pleasant thing to have dropped on your big toe, and the loader was realising it.

The sergeant, relieved to find it was nothing worse, had no room for sympathy.

"Next time, you must ask Danny to be more careful," he grinned. "Forget it, and pull on the end of this track."

While the driver lifted one end of the track from the ground, his companions heaved on the other. The two new plates were joined up and fastened with a pin where the ends met. They tightened up the idler wheel adjustment, and with a grunt of satisfaction the sergeant stepped back a pace to survey the result.

"Bit slack," he said critically to the driver. "What do you think?"

"Good enough to limp home with," returned the driver.

"It's got to be. We're damned lucky to have done as much. Have to go careful on the turns."

Allowing for the spell when they were taking cover from the dive-bomber, only three-quarters of an hour had elapsed since they started the repairs. The sergeant had every reason to congratulate himself. He was fully aware they had done a damn good job in the circumstances—providing the track held. His satisfaction was augmented a moment later when the flaps of the turret opened and the taciturn gunner thrust his head out.

" O.K.," he said, announcing the final extinction of the pestilent machine-gun.

The driver climbed into his seat. There came the whirr of the starter motor. The engine spluttered and roared. In the clear air the fumes of the exhaust smelt warm and strong. Sniffing them luxuriously, the sergeant decided it was the best stink that had come his way for many a long day.

The arrival of a couple of H.E. shells that burst not far away cut short his enjoyment.

" Mount," he cried, and hastily followed the loader into the turret. He donned the headphones and held the microphone to his lips. In a second or two he would know whether they were going to get through.

" Driver . . . advance . . ." he shouted.

The tank moved slowly forward.

" Right . . . Right . . . Steady . . ."

A thrill of exultation swept through the sergeant as he found the tank behaving correctly. Grand to be under way again ! Once more that thrilling sensation of security and invincibility took possession of him. Again he felt like a destiny handing out inexorable fate, all-powerful, untouchable. His one regret was that he had to make his way back to " Rally."

The loader was crooning away, " Don't sign on for twenty-one " unchecked.

XI—THE LADY OF THE GUN-PIT

SHE may be said to have thrown in her lot with the Allies at an auspicious moment.

It was the beginning of the Wavell push. Moving up in support of the Rajputana Rifles, the machine-gun section had just conducted a highly successful shoot on a battery of Italian field guns at the fortified Nibeiwa Camp, in the open desert, some fifteen miles south of Sidi Barrani. The enemy gunners were shot to ribbons, and the Indians stormed the position with the bayonet. Tanks suddenly charged into the camp from nowhere. The Italian Commander was shot dead, and in less than no time the defenders had surrendered. Over two thousand prisoners dropped into the bag. A large number of guns and huge supplies were captured. It was a smart morning's work, and the machine-gun section was elated at its contribution to the entertainment. Later in the day they stowed away their two guns and kit into a couple of trucks, and struck off across the sand dunes to new positions.

In the rear truck the small lean corporal, who was Number One on the gun, occupied the second driver's seat, with the rest of the gun crew sitting behind. As the December afternoon wore on it began to strike a bit coldish, and the men buttoned up their greatcoats, and wound scarves up to their ears. For some time they bumped on over the featureless desert. The corporal commenced treating the company to a vivid, not to say morbid, description of how, after the surrender at Nibeiwa, he had taken a peep into the tent of General Maletti, the slain Italian Commander.

"They'd just dumped the poor bloke on a camp bed," he said. "There he was, stretched on his back with his jaw dropped and his eyes wide open as if he hadn't got over his surprise yet. There was a little table by the side of the bed covered with his medals, all glittering. Hadn't had time to put 'em on, I suppose. His right arm was hanging over the bed . . . like this. And what d'you think he still held between his fingers? A half-smoked cigarette. He . . ."

The narrative was violently interrupted by a shout from one of the men behind.

"Hi . . . Stop . . . Stop . . ."

Thinking his veracity was being impugned, the corporal looked over his shoulder.

"Stop what?" he exclaimed indignantly. "I'm telling you the truth."

"Stop the truck," shouted the man, who was the feeder of the gun. And the others joined in.

"Why?"

"I want to pick up this dog."

"What dog?"

"Been running behind us for over a mile. Poor little devil. Looks knocked to the wide."

The driver pulled up. The feeder jumped down and returned carrying a desert dog in his arms. It was about the size of a small collie, white and black, with a longish coat and a long, bushy tail. Its sharp, pointed muzzle resembled that of a Pomeranian. The half-starved creature stood in the truck nervously, intently watching its new companions with a pair of nice brown, intelligent-looking and friendly eyes. All the men took to it on the spot.

"What sort of breed would you say it was?" said the feeder, patting it affectionately.

"Breed!" echoed the loader scornfully. "You don't know much about dogs. That animal's no breed. It's what they call a pie-dog . . . a thief."

"I've seen many a bloke who don't look so honest, all the same," returned the feeder, already touchy on the score of his new possession. "Besides, I don't believe it's a pie-dog. Look how tame it is. And what about that hand-made leather collar it's wearing?"

"Run away from some Arabs, I expect. . . . And another thing, too. It ain't a dog at all. It's a bitch."

"What makes her keep on shivering?" said one of the men. "Can't keep a limb still. . . . Cold?"

"Frightened," was the verdict of the all-sapient loader. "Scared out of her skin by the noise of the shelling."

"What are we going to do with her?" inquired the corporal.

"Keep her," replied the feeder.

As everyone, including the loader, expressed hearty concurrence, the truck resumed its journey with the dog of no breed sitting on the feeder's lap wrapped in a blanket. The men plied her with scraps of bully-beef, which she devoured ravenously. Later on, the feeder hopped out of the truck again and picked up a discarded Italian mess tin which they filled with some of the precious water stored in the twelve-gallon copper cistern fitted into the floor of the truck. After swallowing this the dog ceased to tremble quite so much. While the men petted and talked to it, her big eyes gleamed more friendly than ever and her sharp, intelligent face followed with interest their slightest movement.

" Pretty cute dog, that, whatever it is," commented the corporal. " Nice-tempered, too. Seems to have taken to us."

" What are we going to call her ? " asked the loader.

All the men except the feeder started to suggest appropriate names. The loader shook his head.

" There's only one name suitable for a bitch," he announced dogmatically. " Lady. . . . That's her name."

" Her name's Nell," interposed the feeder, quietly but firmly.

" Who said so ? "

" I did. Who was it jumped out and got her ? I suppose I've got a right to name my own dog."

" Your dog ! . . . Your dog ! . . . Our dog, if you don't mind," everyone began to protest vigorously.

" Aw, let him call it Nell if he wants to," exclaimed the loader. " I suppose it's the name of his girl. Wonder how she'd like the idea of her name being given to a pie-dog," he added, unable to resist a chance of teasing the feeder. " Not very flattering."

And that is how Nell came to join the Army of the Nile. The same evening when the truck reached its destination, the feeder dismounted, and with the dog still wrapped in a blanket in his arms, ran straight into the Platoon Commander.

" What have you got there ? " inquired the latter.

" Our new mascot, sir," replied the feeder uneasily.

" Haven't you had enough luck already ? " laughed the Platoon Commander.

He began to fondle the dog, which responded by nuzzling its nose into the palm of his hand.

" Seems to have taken quite a fancy to me," he said, flattered. " All right. You can keep it so far as I am concerned."

*   *   *

Sidi Barrani and Maktila had fallen. As an interlude to battle, the machine-gun crew, with the rest of the platoon, were detailed to mount guard over an Italian prisoners' camp a few miles east of Buq Buq. It comprised between fifteen hundred and two thousand men, stragglers who had been rounded up in the desert in the last few days by reconnaissance parties. And more were still coming in. There had been no time to construct a wire cage. The prisoners were all herded together in a rough-and-ready rectangle, with a Vickers gun mounted at each corner in case of trouble. From their cowed and dispirited appearance this seemed unlikely. Such unruliness as did occur was among themselves when the lorries brought up the water ration. Fearful of not getting a share of the precious fluid, the prisoners sometimes stampeded, and in the general mix up water-bottles got knocked out of people's hands and trampled under foot. Now, to the Italian soldier in the desert his water-bottle is his most precious possession. Far more precious than his rifle. He is ready to guard it with his life. So on these occasions threats and blows were freely exchanged, and the sentries had to adopt a firm hand.

With fixed bayonets and revolvers, the machine gunners did sentry-go day and night up and down the sides of the rectangle. They were not too enamoured of the job. A soft time was all right in its way. But this one was accompanied by a stench from the herd of prisoners that dulled their appetite for bully-beef stew. It hung over the camp, day and night, like a poisonous miasma, the evil exhalation from hundreds of filthy, unwashed and verminous bodies. It was an eye-opener to the British soldier to make acquaintance with the low standard of personal hygiene that satisfied Mussolini's warriors. They could understand the tattered, dust-stained uniforms, the worn-out boots, the unshaven chins. These were the common insignia of war. But the accumulated filth and vermin was quite another matter.

So thought the machine-gun feeder as he marched up and down his side of the rectangle during his tour of duty towards the end of the third afternoon. Blessed with a stomach on the sensitive side, he kept sniffing the air fastidiously and then spitting the taste out of his mouth. Unfortunately for him, the breeze was blowing the perfume straight in his direction. Earlier on there had been a bit of a dust-storm, and a sort of thin yellow fog still hung over the camp, like a manifestation of the unwholesome vapours rising from below. The sentry endeavoured to give his charges as wide a berth as possible. But now and again prisoners would insist on coming up in a friendly way and press him to accept a " souvenir "—the said souvenirs being cheap metal medallions bearing the head of Mussolini. These medallions were, in fact, scattered over the desert, where the prisoners had flung them, some for diplomatic reasons, some from a genuine sudden loss of interest in the personality of their Duce. As the platoon by this time had acquired all the Mussolini medallions it was ever likely to want, the sentry met all advances with a curt, " Keep it yourself," and moved off quickly.

At his side trotted Nell. A few days as mascot to the machine-gunners had transformed her from a pitiable-looking outcast into quite a highly respectable specimen of the canine tribe. Well-washed, well-combed, and well fed, she appeared not unconscious of her new dignities. Her behaviour, as she kept pace with the sentry, could not have been more correct if she had just walked out of Cruft's. She kept her sharp, intelligent face fastened on him to divine his slightest intention, halted when he halted, and about-turned when he about-turned. As was only befitting, she regarded the feeder as her natural protector. The rest of the gun crew did not object to this. It placed on him the responsibility for her well-being, and the task of frequently tramping some miles across the desert with her to the nearest water-point when she was in need of a bath. But they firmly resisted any signs on the part of the feeder to establish proprietary rights in the dog, as he seemed persistently inclined to. ⌐ " Our dog," they corrected him voci-ferously on such occasions.

The sight of Nell doing sentry-go amused the Italian prisoners immensely. They shouted to one another to come and see it. Anything that provided a diversion in their present state was welcome. So they crowded along the side of the rectangle as Nell and the feeder paced up and down, making humorous comments which he could not understand, but which he interpreted favour-ably. He felt quite proud of the attention his comrade attracted. But he was not so pleased when the prisoners made overtures to pet Nell. These he roughly rebuked, moved both by jealousy and a fear lest the dog might be decoyed away.

He paced up the side of the rectangle, thinking it was about time he was relieved, when, from somewhere behind, he heard, above the general hum of chatter and conversation, a sharp call in Italian, two words which were repeated. He guessed it was some prisoner calling to Nell. But he walked on, taking no notice. It had been happening constantly during the afternoon. How-ever, a moment or two later there followed a loud burst of laughter. He glanced down and discovered that Nell was no longer by his side. Looking behind, he was just in time to see her bushy black and white tail disappear-ing into the crowded pen of prisoners. Fearful of losing her amidst this seething mob, and indignant at the trick that had been played on him, he plunged at once into the evil-smelling crowd, angrily pushing his way through the amused Italians in the direction in which Nell had dis-appeared. It took some time to find her, and he had to dig quite deeply into the heart of the camp. Finally he came up with her in the middle of a group of laughing prisoners. A big, fat Italian infantryman whose dirty flesh showed through the rents in his tattered olive-green uniform, was bending down petting Nell. It did not mollify the feeder to note that she appeared already on friendly terms with her abductors. He scowled heavily at the big Italian.

" This your dog ? " he demanded challengingly.

The other showed his teeth in a wide grin.

" No me dog," he replied in English.

" Then next time you just leave the bloody thing alone," ordered the feeder. " I don't like strangers messing about with my dog."

The Italian, still grinning in a friendly way, pointed down at Nell.

" Italian collar, Italian dog," he said in explanation.

" Is that so ? " replied the feeder with a stony stare. " Well, I'll tell you something." He tapped himself once or twice on the chest. " English soldier . . ." he announced curtly, and pointing at Nell in mimicry of the other, added : " English dog."

Without more ado he picked Nell up and carried her outside the camp. They resumed their sentry-go. Henceforth he kept a more watchful eye on her. He forgave her readily. But not so her tempters. For the rest of the afternoon he was very brusque indeed with any of the prisoners who sought to thrust their attentions upon her.

Later in the day, when the machine-gun crew were relaxing in their bivouac, the conversation began to revolve, as it often did now, round Nell and her welfare.

" That dog's coming along nicely," remarked the corporal. " She's getting quite fat."

" That canned veal agrees with her," observed the loader. He looked over to the feeder who was sitting with Nell between his knees. " I was noticing this afternoon we're running a bit short of cans," he said. " You ought to scrounge around to-morrow for some more. Can't let the dog starve, you know."

The desert was littered with little 8-ounce tins of veal which had been flung away by the Italians in their

hurried retreat.   It was good stuff, and Nell particularly
appreciated it.   It had been the main article of her diet
for days, apart from Italian biscuits.   The feeder was
in the habit of wandering over the sand when he was
off duty, and collecting a store of cans.   The gun crew
were willing to regard it as his job.   He didn't mind
at all.   There was little he wouldn't do for Nell.   But
this time the loader's tone stung him to protest.

"You've got a nerve, telling me," he said hotly.
"Why don't *you* scrounge round for a change.   I don't
ever remember you taking the trouble to find a meal
for her."

"What's the good of my interfering ? " said the
loader airily.   "You know you wouldn't like it.   And
that reminds me.   You boys noticed anything strange
about that dog ? "

None of them had.

"Well, I have," continued the loader.

"What do you mean by strange? " the feeder demanded
suspiciously.

"Something as shouldn't be about a dog.   Something
unnatural."

"Nell's natural enough," grunted the feeder.

"Then why don't she bark once in a while ? " inquired
the loader darkly.   "Have you ever heard her bark ?
Has any of us ever heard her bark ?   I maintain that
there's something unnatural about a dog that doesn't
bark.   Isn't it their nature to ? "

As soon as the loader mentioned it everyone recalled
that never, all the time she had been with them, had
the dog uttered anything like the semblance of a bark.
The feeder himself was struck by this fact, too.   It
was a bit strange.   But he did not intend to admit it.
Or anything else that might cast the slightest slur on
the merits of Nell.

"There's some dogs whose nature it is not to bark,"
he said.   "Just as there are some blokes whose nature
it is to love the sound of their own voices."

"Maybe, maybe," commented the loader loftily,

overlooking the personal aspersion. " But give me a dog with a bark in it, every time. Shows it's got a bit of life about it. I've got a Manchester terrier at home— barks at the slightest sound. Full of life and spirits, indoors and out. That's the sort of animal I like. Never a dull moment. Keeps the place cheerful."

" When you're at home I bet you have the wireless on all day and the windows wide open," interjected the feeder scornfully.

" D'you know what I did with that dog one day ? " continued the loader, ignoring the interruption and addressing himself to the rest of the company.

" I know what you ought to have done with it," said the feeder, in whose heart there still rankled the aspersion on Nell.

" What ? " inquired the loader incautiously.

" Poisoned it," said the feeder.

The loader looked round the group, a really pained expression on his face.

" Did you hear that ? " he asked. " A nice thing to say to a bloke about an animal he loves. I don't like that."

" And I don't like blokes trying to be funny about my dog," retorted the feeder.

Immediately the usual shout went up from the rest of the gun crew :

" Our dog, if you don't mind. Our dog."

" Yes, our dog," the loader joined in. " Here, Nell. Good girl. Come over here for a change."

The feeder reluctantly separated his knees, releasing Nell for general circulation. She wandered from one to the other of the men, getting a biscuit here and there, and pleasing them all, as she invariably did, with her intelligent brown eyes and her friendly ways. The loader, who always made a great fuss of her, began to tickle her under the throat. Suddenly he stopped, and exclaimed :

" What's this here ? "

A moment or two later he was exhibiting something he had detached from her collar where it had remained concealed by her long coat.

"A Musso medal," cried the corporal. "Who tied that on her?"

The feeder knew that every eye was turned upon him. He felt himself reddening in the face.

"I know," the loader addressed him indignantly. "You've been letting our dog mix with them flea-bitten dagos. I bet she's full of lice and fever by now."

"She bolted into the camp after a bloke called her," explained the feeder self-consciously. "She's all right. She wasn't inside a minute before I hauled her out."

"And what's more," pursued the loader relentlessly, "you let one of them dagos clap Musso's hall-mark on her under your very nose."

"I'll know that funny bastard if I set eyes on him again," said the feeder darkly.

"Very likely. But what I'm thinking is, ought we to trust you to take our dog out again? I'm not so sure," the loader said, with quite impressive gravity.

*   *   *

For seven days the machine-gun crew had been lying outside Bardia in a defensive position dug in the sand. They were now attached to a company of Australian infantry, whom they were to support when the grand attack on the town was launched. There were signs that this would not long be delayed. On both sides the artillery fire was increasing in intensity, and the enemy had been driven to a desperate and futile dive-bombing attack on the troops that were being massed outside the perimeter ready for the assault.

In the interval that had elapsed since they stood guard over the prisoners' camp, the machine-gun crew had been in action several times, and had no reason to find fault with the efficacy of their new mascot. Nell had accompanied them through the thick of all the fighting. She was now a familiar figure in the gun-pit, and all the men were proud of her. She had also picked up a little useful knowledge. Whenever the gun-pit was being heavily shelled, as it frequently was in those final days outside Bardia, she flattened herself out till her belly nearly scraped the ground, and crawled into the nearest slit trench. On these occasions her favourite device was to thrust her head as far as possible under the stomach of one of the gunners who was taking cover. There she would lie, trembling in every limb. But she was never known to whimper or make the slightest sound. After the shelling was over she emerged a bit pathetic-looking, but as docile-tempered as ever, though it was sometimes hours before her shivering fit subsided. The gun crew, understanding how sensitive she was, gave her full marks for pluck. The fact that she shared their dangers without complaining endeared her to them more than ever.

Zero hour at last. . . . In the darkness before the dawn the machine-gun crew in their truck dashed off across the desert towards their starting line. On the floor in the back of the truck sat Nell, under the legs of the feeder. After proceeding for three miles they reached the white tape, and as soon as they crossed it the full force of the British barrage burst with the violence of a hundred thunderstorms. Sixty-pounders, 25-pounders, 15-pounders, and naval guns all opened up together with ear-splitting effect. Added to this was the reply of the enemy batteries, and the incessant rattle of their Breda guns as the tracer bullets carved up the black sky with red, white and green lines. The ground quivered under the terrible concussion of the bursting shells.

Amid this colossal uproar the machine-gun truck tore forward in the darkness. They passed some groups of infantrymen creeping up behind the barrage, drove through the gap in the wire, got safely over the tank trap and then turned left to get into touch with their Australian company. It was at this moment that the driver, glued to the wheel, and straining his eyes to see in the darkness, said to the corporal beside him :

" Blimey, if I don't think we've got a rat in this truck. Something's crawling about my feet. Just put your hand down and see."

The corporal did as requested. His hand encountered something soft and furry, that uttered a tiny squeal as he touched it. He lifted it up gingerly in front of his face for inspection.

" It's a pup ! " he cried, astounded.

At the same moment one of the men in the rear of the truck shouted :

" Nell's had pups. . . . They're wandering all over the floor. I've just picked up one. What are we going to do, Corporal ? "

The event was so staggering in the circumstances that the corporal had no suggestions to offer. The astonished feeder put his hand under his legs and discovered that Nell was no longer there.

" She's gone," he exclaimed in dismay.

" No, she hasn't," said a voice. " She's over here. She's running round looking for the pups."

Everybody except the driver now began to grope about the floor of the truck in the darkness, in search of Nell's lost progeny. This was not easy. The truck was stacked with machine-gun kit, and they dared not strike a match or flash a torch. Every now and then a hand encountered Nell, busy on the same quest. Meanwhile the truck drove forward into the defences of Bardia with the terrific battle raging around them.

" Can you beat it ? " exclaimed the loader in disgust. " There's to-morrow, and the day after, and the day after that. And that bloody dog must go and choose a time like this, when we're up to our necks in a fight, to throw a litter."

The feeder, hearing his favourite assailed, brindled up at once.

" It isn't her fault."

" Then whose fault is it ? " demanded the loader. " Mine ? "

" It's this blasted row," said the feeder. " Shelling always upsets her."

" Lot of difference between being upset and cluttering us up with a bunch of pups when we're going into action,"

grumbled the loader. " I always said there was something strange about her."

" No, there isn't. She's normal enough, poor bitch,"
the feeder retorted, with a touch of sentiment.

" Bitch is correct," said the loader tersely.

While the truck bounced and bumped along the men
continued to fish among the kit for the newly-born pups,
guided now and then in the darkness by faint squeals.
For the time being the battle took second place in their
thoughts. The main business now was to straighten
out Nell's little affair and insure that mother and offspring
got a fair chance to " do well." The enemy shells were
bursting round them at frequent intervals. But their
chief worry was to avoid accidentally treading on any
of Nell's family. How many this numbered they did
not know. But after a very exhaustive search they
decided that four must be the full total. One of these
proved to be dead, and was thrown out of the truck.
The loader wouldn't allow this to be done till he had
personally satisfied himself that life was extinct. Having
exhausted his grouse, he was as eager as the rest of the
men for the welfare of Nell and her young. He had
business instincts, too.

" We'll rear these pups," he said. " And maybe make
a bit out of them. Ought to be no difficulty in selling
them. It isn't every day you can buy a pup that's been
born in the middle of a battle. Makes them a bit of a curio."

The corporal suddenly burst out laughing.

" What's funny about that ? " asked the loader.

" I'm thinking about how we used to pride ourselves
on the way we were fattening her up," he replied. " We
thought it was that Italian veal. But it wasn't. She
must have been like that when we first picked her up.
I'm surprised you didn't notice it, seeing as you claim
to know so much about dogs."

The loader was silenced. He helped the feeder to
spread a leather jacket on the floor at the back of the
truck, over which they placed some empty sandbags.
They carefully arranged the three surviving pups on top

and put Nell on top of them. She settled down at once to lick them all over.

"See that?" said the loader quite solemnly. "And all the time she's shivering in terror herself owing to this bloody noise. Just shows you what a wonderful thing nature is."

Shortly afterwards the truck pulled up. The gun crew jumped down, unloaded their kit and hurried forward into action.

"Look after Nell," they shouted to the driver.

Soon they were covering with their fire the advance of the Australian infantrymen working up against an enemy strong point.

Left behind with the truck to await their return, the driver busied himself making a more comfortable bed for the mother and family, with the assistance of an empty Italian ammunition box which he picked up close by.

* * *

After the capture of Bardia the machine-gun crew, with the rest of the victorious army, swept on over the desert towards Tobruk. And it was during this period that Nell fell from grace. In fact, it was not so much a fall as a headlong dive. Which is always the case when angels decide to go into declension.

Nothing had happened to foreshadow this startling lapse in Nell's conduct. She was still as tame, friendly and affectionate as ever. And if she did not give the men so much of her attention as in the past, this was because her time was fully occupied by maternal duties. She spent hours licking the three pups, two of which were black and white, and promised to be exact reproductions of their mother. The third was an all-white one, and for some reason Nell appeared to have made this her favourite. She very seldom left them, and no longer haunted the gun-pit when the crew were dug-in. Sometimes when the truck halted for a spell on the move forward, she would jump out and take a few turns round it for exercise. But she never strayed many yards away. She had now grown so familiar with the truck that as soon as she heard the engine start-up she would jump on without waiting to be called, and immediately make her way to the ammunition box at the rear of the vehicle to assure herself that nothing had befallen her family during her brief absence. When the gunners happened to come under shell-fire nothing could induce Nell to leave her offspring. She watched the men take cover in slit trenches, but no longer accompanied them, as had been her custom. She still shivered with terror at the exploding shells, and her brown eyes assumed a tortured expression that was pitiful to behold. Nevertheless, she remained on guard over her pups, uttering not the slightest whine, despite her torment. The gun crew voted her a model mother all round, and considered she could give lessons in the job to many a human one. Which all helped to intensify the shock they received when she dropped such a tremendous blot on her copybook.

The truck was proceeding over a desert track about half-way between Bardia and Tobruk. It was a bright January day with a cold breeze blowing that raised the dust uncomfortably. At mid-day they halted for dinner, a few yards from a large sangar, which previously had been an enemy outpost, but was now deserted. It was only to be a brief halt, so the men ate their bully-beef and tinned potatoes in the truck. Nell decided she was in need of a stroll, and jumped out.

They had just commenced to eat when a tall, hatchet-faced Australian belonging to the infantry company to which the machine-gunners were attached, approached the truck from the direction of the sangar.

" Bloke round the corner there wants to shake hands with you," he said casually to the corporal, and passed on without displaying a flicker of further interest in the matter.

The corporal, curious to see who this acquaintance might be, immediately jumped out of the truck and walked over to the sangar, carrying his bully-beef and biscuit sandwich in his hand. He disappeared round the low, stone wall of the sangar, but was not gone long. In a few moments he returned to the truck, a queer look on his face.

"Who was your pal ? " asked the loader.

" Some of these Aussies have a bloody funny sense of humour," said the corporal, sourly.

" Wasn't nobody there ? "

" A bit of somebody," said the corporal. " Just an arm with a hand attached. No sign of who it belonged to."

" One of ours ? "

" No. A dago arm. Poking out of one of their blue cardigans. Gave me quite a turn to see it lying there on the ground with nothing near it."

He looked gloomily at his sandwich and then relinquished it.

" That funny Aussie's taken my appetite away," he added sorrowfully. " I was quite hungry before. I think I'll have a drink of tea instead."

" Go on. . . . Eat up, corporal. Take more than a dago arm to put me off my food," said the loader. Then he began to laugh.

" I'd have given a bit to have seen your face when you walked round that corner," he exclaimed.

The rest of the men began to laugh, too. Finding that they all seemed to be of the same opinion as the Australian, that it was a good joke, the corporal relapsed into a sulky silence.

Their exploitation of the gruesome humours of the incident came to an abrupt termination.

" Almighty God ! . . ." suddenly cried the loader. " Look at that."

He pointed in the direction of the sangar. The gun crew stared, speechless. The model mother, the sweet-tempered, affectionate Nell, whom they all idolised, had dragged from behind the wall of the sangar a human arm with a blue cardigan attached, and was gnawing away at it like a famished wolf. It was a revolting spectacle, and the sight of it made the men feel faintly sick. For a moment they remained spellbound with horror and disgust. The feeder was the first to recover. Without a word being spoken he jumped from the truck, strode across to Nell, took a firm grip on her collar and

tore her from her prey.   At first she seemed inclined to
resist.   Next moment she became her old winning self,
looked up at the feeder with her friendly, trustful brown
eyes, and obediently allowed him to lead her back to the
truck.   He lifted her inside, and she immediately went
over to see how the pups were getting on.

The men in the truck looked at one another uncomfortably.

"Who'd have believed she'd do a thing like that,"
said the corporal, in an almost awestruck voice.

"Only one thing to do with her now," observed the
loader decisively.   "Shoot her."

A glum silence fell upon the men.

"Why?" demanded the feeder, firing up at once in
defence of the delinquent.

"Because she's reverted to type.   Now she's tasted
human flesh she'll always be bad."

"She's all right," asserted the feeder stoutly.   "It
was only an accident.   Look at her now.   Just the same
as she has always been."

The loader glanced round the group of shocked faces.

"Well, I don't know how you other blokes feel about
it," he said.   "But I'd never be able to look at that dog
again without getting the creeps.   If ever I get my
packet I'd like to be buried face and all.   I'd never feel
sure of it with that dog about."

"You set a hell of a store on your face," shouted the
feeder.

"It's too good for a meal for a cannibal pie-dog,
anyway," retorted the loader.

"I can't understand it," mused the corporal.   "It
isn't as if she was hungry.   Look how we feed her.
Never a day without her can of veal.   And sometimes two."

"That's just the trouble," interposed the feeder
eagerly, overrunning himself in his haste to find excuses
for his favourite.   "She got tired of that canned stuff,
and was tempted by the chance of a bit of fresh meat.
It's only natural."

"And ain't I tired of canned stuff?   Ain't we all

tired of canned stuff ? " cried the loader. " But we don't go round wanting to eat people. But you're right about it being natural. That's where you hit the nail dead on the head. It's so natural that she'll do it again. Unless we shoot her."

" I'm not having her shot," the feeder announced with determination.

" You're not the only one that has a say," replied the loader. " Don't forget that it's our dog, not your dog."

They settled down to a discussion upon the fate of Nell in which the feeder took no part. Having fully made up his mind he was not going to let Nell be shot, he wasted no further breath on the matter. The discussion itself was an odd one. The men conducted it with the gravity becoming an occasion when a life was at stake. But each of them, including the loader, knew in his heart all the time that nothing was going to happen to Nell. It was the last thing any of them wanted. They recognised the heinous character of her behaviour. It had disturbed them considerably. It wasn't a thing to be passed over too lightly. They had to make some show of conscience. But as for shooting Nell. . . . Well, of course, that was unthinkable.

The corporal provided them with the desired get-out.

" We're forgetting about the pups," he said suddenly. " If we did away with Nell, they'd die."

" Yes. That makes it awkward," agreed the loader. " Like punishing the innocent for the guilty."

" They're too young for us to rear them," added the corporal. " And Nell's a first-rate mother."

" Couldn't be better," agreed the loader. " Well, boys, it looks like a reprieve on account of a young family. Let's hope the criminal will mend her ways. All those in favour . . ."

It was carried unanimously. And instantaneously.

*　　　*　　　*

The machine-gun crew were in defensive positions outside Tobruk, which was completely invested by the

British forces all along the thirty miles of the outer perimeter. By now, the three pups had their eyes open. In the daytime they crawled about on a blanket the men had pegged down on the sand just to the rear of the gun-pit. When they were inclined to wander off it, Nell cuffed them back again. They were lively little creatures, and promised well. The crew supplemented Nell's efforts by feeding them from tins of Italian evaporated milk which they retrieved from deserted dug-outs. It agreed with them splendidly. At night, mother and family slept in a hole dug in the sand, wrapped in a couple of blankets, for it was the middle of January and could be very chilly in the small hours.

The business instincts of the loader proved sound. Already the black-and-white pups had been bespoke by two Australian officers, who were only waiting till they were ready to leave their mother. The unusual circumstances of the birth had, in fact, given them no little celebrity among the troops in the vicinity, and it was quite a common occurrence for visitors to walk over and inspect them. As the pups grew in size and playfulness, the men became a little sorry that they had arranged to part with them. But there was no help for it. Besides, they felt they would never become as fond of them as they were of Nell. She was their first love, and remained so. Her one lapse had been completely forgiven, and almost forgotten. Among themselves, it was regarded as in very bad taste to allude to it. And they kept it an inviolable secret from strangers. On her part, Nell seemed desirous of wiping out the memory of her disgrace by displaying herself more affectionate and winning than ever. They laughed at the idea of ever parting with her.

" Nell's with us for as long as this war lasts," said the loader one day, thus voicing the sentiments of all of them. " And afterwards, we'll have to toss up for her."

It was a bright sunny afternoon, with nothing much doing. There had been some shelling earlier in the day. As usual, it had sent Nell into one of her shivering fits. She was still trembling a little as she lay on the blanket

in the sunshine with the pups nosing under her belly.
In the gun-pit the crew sat chatting and idly watching
the smoke-puffs from enemy ack-ack shells, bursting in
an otherwise speckless blue sky around an Army Co-
operation plane that hovered over the defences taking
photographs of the mine-fields.

In the crawl trench just behind the gun-pit suddenly
appeared the Platoon Commander, and the corporal went
to meet him."

" Nice afternoon, sir."

" Yes, corporal.   Nothing happened to you this
morning, I suppose ?   The section on the left had a
mounting damaged by a shell splinter."

" So I heard, sir," replied the corporal, faintly wondering why the Platoon Commander should bother to come
up to tell him such ancient history.

They stood for a few moments watching the photo-
graphing plane.

" I'm glad to see them getting on with that job," the
Platoon Commander observed.   " The sooner it's done,
the sooner we'll be in Tobruk."

" When d'you think we'll be putting in the attack,
sir ? "

" Can't say.   Not before we get the new maps of the
defences.   Depends on those fellows upstairs."

He nodded towards the reconnaissance plane which
was now flying daringly low.   The corporal said nothing.
He still had the impression that this was all small talk,
and waited for the real object of the visit.   He followed
the Platoon Commander's gaze to the blanket on the
sand where Nell and her family were disporting themselves.

" Pups coming along nicely, sir, aren't they ? " he
observed.

The Platoon Commander averted his glance quickly.

" Look here, corporal," he began awkwardly.   " I've
got something unpleasant to tell you.   Something that
I'm afraid you and the men won't like.   You've got to
destroy those dogs."

" Destroy the pups, sir ! "

" And the mother."

" Destroy Nell ! . . ." The corporal could hardly believe his ears.

" I know it's a blow," went on the Platoon Commander. " But it can't be helped. There's a General Order from the Brigadier that all dogs are to be destroyed. There has been too much barking at night when the patrols go out. It gives warning to the enemy. Some of the patrols have been cut up badly, in consequence."

" But that don't apply to Nell, sir," said the corporal desperately. " She never barks. It's the strange thing about her. She hasn't barked once, all the time we've had her."

" I'm afraid there's no exception," said the Platoon Commander. " It's a General Order. Tell the men I'm very sorry, indeed."

He turned and went off, leaving the corporal with the unpleasant job of breaking the news to the gun-crew. It dropped on them like a thunderbolt. At first they refused to believe it. They thought it a very bad joke on the part of the corporal. When the truth dawned on them they broke out into violent protestations.

" Don't attack me," shouted the harassed corporal, fiercely. " D'you think I want to lose Nell any more than you do ? "

" Didn't you tell him that she never barks ? " urged the loader. " Didn't you tell him that fifty patrols could go out and she'd never breathe a sound ? "

" He said there were no exceptions. It's a General Order signed by the Brigadier."

" Then the Brigadier will have to bloody well shoot her himself," exclaimed the loader, angrily. " I won't. And neither will any of you."

He strode out of the gun-pit across to the blanket, and sat down to fondle the doomed animal. The feeder was too saddened to trust himself to go near her. A general gloom settled upon the gun-pit. Resent it as much as they liked, each man in his heart of hearts knew that the fate of Nell was sealed. It was incredible, but it was going to happen. Like the loader, each man was firmly resolved, that whatever the result, his hand should not be that of executioner.

That night Nell slept, as usual, wrapped in a blanket with her family in the hole by the side of the gun-pit.

Next day was Sunday, another brilliant day, but with the breeze freshening and threatening a dust-storm later on. During the afternoon an Australian infantryman wandered over to the gun position to see the dogs of whom he had heard so much. They told him the sad news.

" Ye-ah. I can understand you don't fancy the job yourselves," he drawled. " Would you like me to fix 'em for you ? "

" When ? "

" Now. No time like the present. As they've got to go, they may as well go quickly."

The gun-crew mournfully agreed that this was a fact.

" I've killed hundreds of 'em," continued the Australian. " I used to work on a greyhound track in Sydney. It won't take long. Get one of your blokes to dig a grave where you want it."

One of the men reluctantly took a shovel and began digging a hole in the desert several yards away. The Australian surveyed his victims, tumbling over one another in play on the blanket, with a professional eye.

" Pups first," he said. " Seems a pity. They *are* nice little chaps."

His solemn audience agreed that they were indeed far too nice for the fate about to befall them, and uttered unprintable things about General Orders.

" Better take the old girl round the other side of the gun-pit," advised the master of ceremonies.

The feeder picked Nell up in his arms and carried her out of sight of the proceedings.

One by one, the expert lifted the pups up by the ears, and as they dangled administered a smart rabbit-punch on the back of the neck with the edge of his right hand. To all appearance they died swiftly and painlessly. The gun-crew looked on in a stony silence.

" For the big' un more preparations are needed," said the Australian. " Got a stake ? And a bit of rope ? And I'll borrow one of your handkerchiefs."

All were forthcoming. The Australian drove the stake firmly into the ground. He went to the other side of the gun-pit and returned leading Nell. The men felt like traitors when they saw her trotting obediently by his side and looking up in his face with her friendly, trustful brown eyes. How many times had she not looked up at them in exactly the same way. . . .

Docile and sweet-tempered as ever, she allowed herself to be tied to the stake without protest. The handkerchief was bound over her eyes. The vivid sunshine threw her black shadow sharply on the white, powdery earth. The gun-crew, hating to look on but compelled to by a morbid fascination, watched the scene from the gun-pit in a moody bitterness. All except the feeder. He remained out of sight.

The Australian unslung his rifle, placed it close to the side of Nell's head, and pulled the trigger. She gave a violent stagger, seemed to fall into her shadow, and lay still.

" Not a whimper. . . . Not a squeal . . ." the loader breathed hoarsely. " What a dog, boys ! . . . What a dog ! . . ."

On the other side of the gun-pit the feeder lay on his back, hands under his head, staring at the blue sky. He heard the shot. A series of little pictures flitted through his brain. Nell, half-starved and panting behind their truck on the day they first picked her up. . . . Nell trotting beside him on sentry-go at the prisoners' camp. . . . Nell licking her newly-born pups as they raced into the hell at Bardia. . . . Nell, looking at him so affectionately and obediently, as he pulled her away from the dago arm. . . .

He stared at the blue sky harder than ever.